THE CONSTRUCTION OF BUILDINGS

Volume 1
CONSTRUCTION AND MATERIALS

FOURTH EDITION

R. BARRY

ARIBA

The English Language Book Society
and Granada   London

Granada Publishing Limited

First published in Great Britain 1958 by Crosby Lockwood & Son Ltd
Second edition 1962, reprinted 1964, 1965, 1968
Third edition (metric) 1969, reprinted 1971

Reprinted by Granada Publishing Limited
in Crosby Lockwood Staples 1972, 1974, 1975, 1979

Fourth edition 1980 by Granada Publishing -- Technical Books Division

ELBS edition first published 1975
ELBS edition reprinted 1977, 1978, 1979
ELBS edition of 4th edition 1980

Granada Publishing Limited
Frogmore, St Albans, Herts AL2 2NF
and
3 Upper James Street, London W1R 4BP

Copyright © R. Barry, 1958, 1962, 1969 and 1980

ISBN 0 246 11491 6

Printed in Great Britain by Richard Clay (The Chaucer Press) Ltd, Bungay, Suffolk

The Construction of Buildings

Volume 1

SOME OTHER ELBS LOW-PRICED EDITIONS

Anderson, Leaver, Alexander and Rawlings	MATERIALS SCIENCE	*Nelson*
Bannister and Raymond	SURVEYING	*Pitman*
Barry	THE CONSTRUCTION OF BUILDINGS, Vols. I-V	*Granada Technical*
Blyth and de Freitas	A GEOLOGY FOR ENGINEERS	*Edward Arnold*
Burnside	ELECTROMAGNETIC DISTANCE MEASUREMENT	*Granada Technical*
Case and Chilver	STRENGTH OF MATERIALS AND STRUCTURES	*Edward Arnold*
Chudley	CONSTRUCTION TECHNOLOGY, Vols. I–IV	*Longman*
Coates, Coutie and Kong	STRUCTURAL ANALYSIS	*Nelson*
Constructional Steel Research and Development Organisation	STEEL DESIGNERS' MANUAL	*Granada Technical*
Dugdale	SURVEYING	*Macdonald & Evans*
Fisher	WALLS	*Macmillan*
Hart	ENGINEERING DRAWING WITH PROBLEMS AND SOLUTIONS	*Hodder & Stoughton*
Jeffrey	MATHEMATICS FOR ENGINEERS AND SCIENTISTS	*Nelson*
John	INTRODUCTION TO ENGINEERING MATERIALS	*Macmillan*
Lambert	STRUCTURAL STEELWORK	*Macdonald & Evans*
Launder	FOUNDATIONS	*Macmillan*
Marshall and Nelson	STRUCTURES	*Pitman*
Owen	ROOFS	*Macmillan*
Pascoe	AN INTRODUCTION TO THE PROPERTIES OF ENGINEERING MATERIALS	*Van Nostrand (U.K.)*
Ryder	STRENGTH OF MATERIALS	*Macmillan*
Smith	CONSTRUCTION SCIENCE	*Longman*
Smith	SOIL MECHANICS	*Macdonald & Evans*
Tomlinson	FOUNDATION DESIGN AND CONSTRUCTION	*Pitman*

CONTENTS

METRIC EDITIONS: NOTE

For linear measure all measurements are shown in either metres or millimetres. A decimal point is used to distinguish metres and millimetres, the figures to the left of the decimal point being metres and those to the right millimetres. To save needless repetition, the abbreviations 'm' and 'mm' are not used, with one exception. The exception to this system is where there are at present only metric equivalents in decimal fractions of a millimetre. Here the decimal point is used to distinguish millimetres from fractions of a millimetre, the figures to the left of the decimal point being millimetres and those to the right being fractions of a millimetre. In such cases the abbreviation 'mm' will follow the figures e.g. 203.2 mm.

R. Barry

ACKNOWLEDGEMENTS

The drawings in this revised edition are the work of my friend and colleague Ross Jamieson.

In the preparation of this revised edition I have had advice and assistance from colleagues in the Faculty of the Built Environment, formerly Brixton School of Building, Polytechnic of the South Bank.

The following tables are included by permission of HMSO: table 3 on page 4 is reproduced from *The Building Regulations* and table 6 on page 34 has been adapted from a table in the *Building Research Establishment Digest*, **160**.

Tables 1 and 2 on page 2, table 4 on page 8, table 7 on page 39 and table 9 on page 54 are extracts from British Standard Codes of Practice and are reproduced by permission of BSI, 2 Park Street, London WLA 2BS from whom complete copies can be obtained.

CHAPTER ONE

FOUNDATIONS

The foundations of buildings bear on and transmit loads to the ground. The foundation is that part of walls, piers and columns in direct contact with and transmitting loads to the ground. In practice, the concrete base of walls, piers and columns is described as the foundation. The principal foundation types are strip, pad, raft and pile foundations as illustrated in Fig. 1.

It will be seen that a strip foundation is a continuous strip of concrete under walls, a pad an isolated base under piers and columns, a raft a continuous base under the whole of the building, and a pile a concrete column or pillar cast in or driven into the ground to support a concrete base or ground beam.

Ground is the general term for the earth's surface, which varies in composition within the two main groups, rocks and soils. Rocks include the hard, rigid, strongly-cemented geological deposits such as granite, sandstone and limestone, and soils the comparatively soft, loose, uncemented geological deposits such as gravel, sand and clay. Unlike rocks, soils compact under the compression of the foundation loads of buildings.

FUNCTIONAL REQUIREMENTS

A foundation should be designed to transmit the loads of the building to the ground so that there is, at most, only a limited settlement of the building into the ground. A building whose foundation is on sound rock will suffer no measurable settlement whereas a building on soil will suffer settlement into the ground by the compression of the soil under the foundation loads. Foundations should be designed so that settlement into the ground is limited and uniform under the whole of the building. Some settlement of a building on a soil foundation is inevitable as the increasing loads on the foundation, as the building is erected, compress the soil. This settlement must be limited to avoid damage to service pipes and drains connected to the building. Bearing capacities for various rocks and soils are assumed and these capacities should not be exceeded in the design of the foundation to limit settlement. These bearing capacities are set out in table 1 on page 2.

In theory, if the foundation soil were uniform and foundation bearing pressure were limited, the building would settle into the ground uniformly as the building was erected, and to a limited extent, and there would be no possibility of damage to the building or its connected services or drains. In practice there are various possible ground movements under the foundation of a

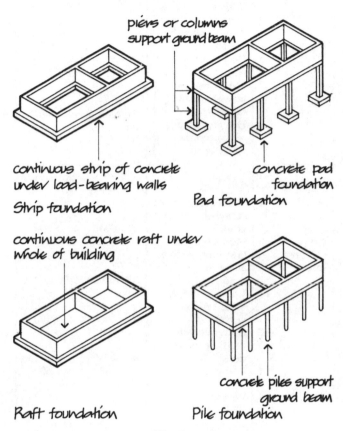

Fig. 1

building that may cause one part of the foundation to settle at a different rate and to a different extent than another part of the foundation. This different or differential settlement must be limited to avoid damage to the superstructure of the building. Some structural forms can accommodate differential or relative foundation movement without damage more than others. A brick wall can accommodate limited differential movement of the foundation or the structure by slight movement of the small brick units and mortar joints, without affecting the function of the wall, whereas a rigid framed structure with rigid panels cannot to the same extent. Foundations are designed to limit differential settlement, the degree to which this limitation has to be controlled or accommodated in the structure depends on the nature of the structure supported by the foundations.

Table 1 Typical Bearing Capacities

Group		Types of rocks and soils	Bearing capacity (kN/m²)	
I	1	Igneous and gneissic rocks in sound condition	10 000	
Rocks	2	Massively-bedded limestones and hard sandstones	4 000	
	3	Schists and slates	3 000	
	4	Hard shales, mudstones and soft sandstones	2 000	
	5	Clay shales	1 000	
	6	Hard solid chalk	600	
	7	Thinly-bedded limestones and sandstones	To be assessed after inspection	
	8	Heavily-shattered rocks and the softer chalks		
			Dry	**Submerged**
II	9	Compact gravel or compact sand and gravel	> 600	> 300
Non-cohesive soils	10	Medium dense gravel or medium dense gravel and sand	200 to 600	100 to 300
	11	Loose gravel or loose sand and gravel	< 200	< 100
	12	Compact sand	> 300	> 150
	13	Medium dense sand	100 to 300	50 to 150
	14	Loose sand	< 100	< 50
III	15	Very stiff boulder clays and hard clays	300 to 600	
	16	Stiff clays	150 to 300	
Cohesive soils	17	Firm clays	75 to 150	
	18	Soft clays and silts	75	
	19	Very soft clays and silts	< 75	
IV	20	Peat	Foundations carried down through peat to a reliable bearing stratum	
V	21	'Made' ground	Should be investigated with extreme care	

Mixed soils – Soils intermediate between the main types given in Table 1 may need to be assessed.
Based on CP 101:1972

ROCKS AND SOILS

Rocks are divided into three broad groups: sedimentary, metamorphic and igneous according to their geological formation. Sedimentary rocks are those formed gradually over thousands of years from particles of calcium carbonate or sand deposited by settlement in bodies of water and gradually compacted into rocks such as sandstone and limestone. Metamorphic rocks are those changed from igneous, sedimentary, or from earth into metamorphic by pressure or heat or both, such as slates and schists. Igneous rocks are those formed by the fusion of minerals under great heat and pressure such as granite, dolerite and basalt. A classification of rocks is set out in table 2.

Table 2 Classification of Rocks

Group	Rock type	
Sedimentary	Sandstones (including conglomerates)	Siliceous / Calcareous / Ferruginous / Argillaceous
	Some hard shales and tuffs	
	Limestones	Massively bedded (including chalk) / Thinly bedded
Metamorphic	Some hard shales / Slates / Schists / Gneisses	
Igneous	Granite / Dolerite / Basalt	

Taken from CP 2001:1957

Soils

Top soil: The surface of much of the land in this country is covered with a layer of top soil or vegetable soil to a depth of about 100–300. Top soil is composed of loose soil, growing plant life and the accumulation of decaying vegetation. As it is very soft it is unsatisfactory as a foundation and it is stripped from the site of buildings.

Subsoil: The soil below the top soil is termed subsoil.

Soils are grouped by reference to the size and nature of the particles and the density of the particular soil. The three broad groups are coarse grained non-cohesive, fine grained cohesive and organic. The nature and behaviour under load of the soils in each group are similar. Organic soils, such as peat, are not generally suitable as a foundation for buildings.

Coarse grained non-cohesive soils such as sands and gravels consist of the coarser largely siliceous unaltered products of rock weathering. They have no plasticity and tend to lack cohesion especially when dry. Under pressure from the loads on foundations the soils in this group compress and consolidate rapidly by some rearrangement of the particles and the expulsion of water. A foundation on coarse grained non-cohesive soils settles rapidly by consolidation of the soil, as the building is erected, so that there is no further settlement once the building is completed. Some sand or sandy soils in waterlogged conditions may expand in frost (frost heave) at and for some distance below the surface. In exposed situations it is practice to carry the foundations down to a depth of 450, which is below the frost line, to avoid ground movement in soils liable to frost heave under and around unheated buildings.

Gravel. A natural coarse grained deposit of rock fragments and finer sand. Many of the particles are larger than 2.

Sand. A natural sediment of granular, mainly siliceous products of rock weathering. Particles are smaller than 2, are visible to the naked eye and the smallest size is 0.06 mm. Sand is gritty, has no real plasticity and can be easily powdered by hand when dry.

Fine grained cohesive soils, such as clay, are a natural deposit of the finest siliceous and aluminous products of rock weathering. Clay is smooth and greasy to the touch, shows high plasticity, dries slowly and shrinks appreciably on drying. Under pressure of the load on foundations clay soils are very gradually compressed by the expulsion of water through the very many, fine capillary paths so that buildings settle gradually during building work and this settlement may continue for some years after the building is completed.

Firm shrinkable clays suffer appreciable vertical and horizontal shrinkage on drying and expansion on wetting. Shrinkage and expansion of firm clays under grass extends to about 1 metre below the surface in Great Britain and up to depths of 4 metres or more below large trees. The extent of volume changes, particularly in firm clay soils, depends on seasonal variations and the proximity of trees and shrubs. The greater the seasonal variation, the greater the volume change. The more vigorous the growth of shrubs and trees in firm clay soils the greater the depth below surface the volume change will occur.

As a rough guide it is recommended that buildings on shallow foundations should not be closer to single trees than the height of the tree at maturity and one-and-a-half times the height at maturity of groups of trees, to reduce the risk of damage to buildings by seasonal volume changes in clay subsoils.

When shrubs and trees are removed to clear a site for building on firm clay subsoils there will, for some years after clearance, be ground recovery as the clay gradually recovers moisture previously withdrawn by the shrubs and trees. This gradual recovery of water by the clay and consequent expansion may take several years. The depth at which the recovery and expansion is appreciable will

be roughly proportional to the height of the trees and shrubs removed, and the design and depth of foundations of buildings must allow for this gradual expansion to limit damage by differential settlement. Similarly if vigorous shrub or tree growth is stopped by removal, or started by planting, near to a building on a firm clay subsoil it is most likely that gradual expansion or contraction of the soil will cause damage to the building by differential movement.

SITE INVESTIGATION AND EXPLORATION

To select a foundation from tables or to design a foundation it is necessary to calculate the loads on the foundation and determine the nature of the subsoil, its bearing capacity, its likely behaviour under seasonal and ground water level changes and the possibility of ground movement. Where the nature of the subsoil is known from geological surveys, adjacent building work or trial pits or borings and the loads on foundations are small, as for single domestic buildings, it is generally sufficient to excavate for foundations and confirm, from the exposed subsoil in the trenches, that the soil is as anticipated.

Under strip and pad foundations there is a significant pressure on the subsoil below the foundation to a depth and breadth of about one-and-a-half times the width of the foundation. If there were, in this area below the foundation, a soil with a bearing capacity less than that below the foundation, then appreciable settlement of the foundation might occur and damage the building. It is important, therefore, to know or ascertain the nature of the subsoil both at the level of the foundation and for some depth below.

The required width of foundation for buildings of up to four storeys may be determined from table 3, on page 4, when the loads and the nature of the subsoil are known. The depth of the foundation below ground will depend on the nature of the subsoil and the need to limit differential settlement due to ground movements.

Where the nature of the subsoil is uncertain or there is a possibility of ground movement or a need to confirm information on subsoils, it is wise to explore the subsoil over the whole of the site of the building.

As a first step it is usual to collect information on soil and subsoil conditions from the County and Local Authority whose local knowledge from maps, geological surveys, aerial photography and works for buildings and services adjacent to the site may in itself give an adequate guide to subsoil conditions. In addition geological maps from the Institute of Geological Sciences, information from local geological societies, ordnance survey maps, mining and river and coastal information may be useful.

A visit to the site and its surroundings should always be made to record everything relevant from a careful examination of the nature of the subsoil, vegetation, evidence of marshy ground, signs of ground water and flooding, irregularities in topography, ground erosion and ditches and flat ground near streams and rivers where there may be soft alluvial soil. A record should be made

Table 3 Minimum Width of Strip Foundations

Type of subsoil	Condition of subsoil	Field test applicable	Minimum width in millimetres for total load in kN/m of loadbearing walling of not more than—					
			20	30	40	50	60	70
I Rock	Not inferior to sandstone, limestone or firm chalk	Requires at least a pneumatic or other mechanically operated pick for excavation	In each case equal to the width of wall					
II Gravel Sand	Compact Compact	Requires pick for excavation. Wooden peg 50 mm square in cross-section hard to drive beyond 150 mm	250	300	400	500	600	650
III Clay Sandy clay	Stiff Stiff	Cannot be moulded with the fingers and requires a pick or pneumatic or other mechanically operated spade for its removal	250	300	400	500	600	650
IV Clay Sandy clay	Firm Firm	Can be moulded by substantial pressure with the fingers and can be excavated with graft or spade	300	350	450	600	750	850
V Sand Silty sand Clayey sand	Loose Loose Loose	Can be excavated with a spade. Wooden peg 50 mm square in cross-section can be easily driven	400	600	Note: Foundations do not fall within the provisions of regulation D7 if the total load exceeds 30 kN/m			
VI Silt Clay Sandy clay Silty clay	Soft Soft Soft Soft	Fairly easily moulded in the fingers and readily excavated	450	650	Note: In relation to types VI and VII, foundations do not fall within the provisions of regulation D7 if the total load exceeds 30 kN/m			
VII Silt Clay Sandy clay Silty clay	Very soft Very soft Very soft Very soft	Natural sample in winter conditions exudes between fingers when squeezed in fist	600	850				

Adapted from The Building Regulations, 1976

of the foundations of old buildings on the site and cracks and other signs of movement in adjacent buildings as evidence of ground movement.

To make an examination of the subsoil on a building site, trial pits or boreholes are excavated. Trial pits are usually excavated by machine or hand to depths of 2–4 metres and at least the anticipated depth of the foundations. The nature of the subsoil is determined by examination of the sides of the excavations. Boreholes are drilled by hand auger or by machine to withdraw samples of soil for examination. Details of the subsoil should include soil type, consistency or strength, soil structure, moisture conditions and the presence of roots at all depths. From the nature of the subsoil the bearing capacity, seasonal volume changes and other possible ground movements are assumed. To determine the nature of the subsoil below the foundation level it is either necessary to excavate trial pits some depth below the foundation or to bore in the base of the trial hole to withdraw samples. Whichever system is adopted will depend on economy and the nature of the subsoil. Trial pits or boreholes should be sufficient in number to determine the nature of the subsoil over and around the site of the building and should be at most say 30 metres apart.

Ground movements that may cause settlement are:

(a) compression of the soil by the load of the building
(b) seasonal volume changes in the soil
(c) ground recovery due to the felling of trees
(d) mass movement in unstable areas such as made-up ground and mining areas where there may be considerable settlement
(e) ground made unstable by adjacent excavations or by dewatering, for example, due to an adjacent road cutting.

It is to anticipate and accommodate these movements that site investigation and exploration is carried out.

Compression of the soil by the load of the building
Differential settlement may occur where there is a significant difference in the loads on adjacent parts of the foundation or where there is a difference in the bearing capacity of the subsoil below the building. From calculations of the anticipated loads on the foundations and from an investigation of the subsoil, differential settlement may be limited in the design of the foundation.

Seasonal volume changes in the soil
Seasonal changes and the withdrawal of moisture by deep-rooted vegetation can cause considerable volume changes in shrinkable clay soils especially after periods of low rainfall. These volume changes can cause severe damage to low rise buildings with foundations near the surface.

The extent of volume changes in shrinkable clay soils and the depth below the surface at which these changes can affect foundations depends largely on whether the building is sited on open ground away from deep-rooted vegetation or close to past, present or future growth of deep-rooted vegetation. A foundation depth of at least 0.9 m on shrinkable clay soils on open ground away from deep-rooted vegetation has been recommended by the Building Research Station for more than twenty-five years and recent experience, such as the severe drought of 1976, has affirmed the wisdom of this recommendation. There appears to be little if any evidence of shrinkage damage to buildings with foundations at or below the recommended depth during periods of drought.

At the recommended depth of at least 0.9 m it is not generally economic to use the traditional strip foundation and hence the narrow strip or trench fill foundation has been used (Fig. 5). A narrow trench 400 wide is excavated by machine and filled with concrete to just below the surface. If the concrete is placed immediately after the excavation there is no need to support the sides of the trench in stiff clays, the sides of the trench will not be washed away by rain and the exposed clay will not suffer volume change by exposure. A narrow strip or trench fill foundation is appreciably cheaper than a traditional strip foundation with foundation walls at these depths.

The foundations of buildings sited adjacent to past, present or future deep-rooted vegetation can be affected at a considerable depth below the surface by the gain or removal of ground moisture and consequent expansion or shrinkage. Appreciable expansion, following the removal of deep-rooted vegetation, may continue for some years as the subsoil gains moisture. Significant seasonal volume change, due to deep-rooted vegetation, will be pronounced during periods of drought and heavy continuous rainfall. The vigorous growth of newly-planted deep-rooted vegetation adjacent to buildings may cause continuous shrinkage in clay soils for some years. The most economical and effective foundation for low rise buildings on shrinkable clays close to deep-rooted vegetation is a system of short-bored piles and ground beams (Fig. 13). The piles should be taken down to a depth below which vegetation roots will not cause significant volume changes in the subsoil. Single deep-rooted vegetation such as shrubs and trees as close as their mature height to buildings, and groups of shrubs and trees one-and-a-half times their mature height to buildings can affect foundations on shrinkable clay subsoils.

Frost heave: Where the water table is high, that is near the surface, soils, such as silts, chalk, fine gritty sands and some lean clays, near the surface may expand when frozen. This expansion, or frost heave, is due to crystals of ice forming and expanding in the soil and so causing frost heave. In this country, ground water near the surface rarely freezes at depths of more than half a metre but in exposed positions on open ground during frost it may freeze up to a depth of one metre. Even in exposed positions during severe frost it is most unlikely that ground water under and adjacent to the foundations of heated buildings will freeze because of the heat stored in the ground under and around the building. There is, therefore, no need to consider the possibility of ground movement due to frost heave under and around heated buildings.

For unheated buildings a foundation depth of 450 is generally sufficient against the possibility of damage by ground movement due to frost heave.

Ground recovery due to the felling of trees
When deep-rooted shrubs and trees are cleared for building on shrinkable clay subsoils there will be a gradual recovery of ground moisture to the soil for some years after the clearance and a consequent gradual expansion of the soil for some depth below the surface. It is necessary, therefore, to take foundations down to a depth at which there will be no significant ground movement by the use, for example, of short-bored piles.

Mass movement in unstable areas such as made-up ground and mining areas
The surface of ground that has been raised by filling or tipping soil, waste or refuse is described as made ground or made-up ground. These filled or fill sites on made-up ground should be avoided for building because of the extreme variability of the nature of the fill and the difficulty of predicting the degree of compaction under load and the variability of compaction and settlement.

Where buildings are to be sited on made-up ground a thorough investigation of the nature of the fill must be carried out to anticipate the likelihood of differential settlement. Single or semi-detached houses on fill should have a raft foundation with an edge beam (see Fig. 10). The construction of terraced houses on fill should be avoided because of the likelihood of differential settlement causing damage by cracking. Larger buildings should be supported by a pile foundation carried down to a firm base. In areas liable to mining subsidence it is wise to seek the advice of the National Coal Board on likely ground movement and recommended foundations. For two storey houses the raft foundation, illustrated in Fig. 9, is often recommended, the thin reinforced concrete raft being laid on a bed of fine granular material to accommodate some ground movement independent of the slab. The CLASP system, illustrated on page 104 of Volume 4, was developed specifically for school buildings on areas liable to mining subsidence.

Concrete in sulphate-bearing soils

Water-soluble sulphates, particularly in clay soils, can combine with the set cement in concrete and cause expansion, cracking and disintegration of concrete. The conditions most favourable to this action are concrete mixes of cements, such as ordinary Portland cement, which combine readily with the sulphates in water-saturated sulphate-bearing soils at or below the water table. The continuous migration of sulphates through ground water to concrete may cause the continuing combination of sulphates with cement and the gradual expansion, cracking and ultimate disintegration of the concrete.

Concrete which is permanently above the water table is unlikely to be attacked by sulphates.

Large sections of thoroughly compacted, dense, impermeable concrete are less subject to attack by sulphates than poorly compacted, pervious concrete into which the sulphates will more readily penetrate in solution in ground water.

Where concrete is placed in sulphate-bearing soils it should consist of one of the sulphate-resisting cements such as sulphate-resisting Portland cement and be fully compacted.

Chemical compounds in fill material have caused disintegration of foundation slabs and brickwork. An impermeable membrane between the fill material, likely to cause damage, and the foundation and slabs will reduce the chance of damage.

FOUNDATION TYPES

The four principal types of foundation are strip, pad, raft and pile foundations as illustrated in Fig. 1.

Strip foundations

Strip foundations consist of a continuous strip, usually of concrete, under load bearing walls. The continuous strip serves as a level base on which the wall is built and is of such a width as is necessary to spread the load on the foundations to an area of subsoil capable of supporting the load without undue compaction. Concrete is the material principally used today for foundations as it can readily be placed, spread and levelled in foundation trenches, to provide a base for walls, and it develops adequate compressive strength as it hardens to support the load on foundations. Before Portland cement was manufactured, strip foundations of brick were common, the brick foundation being built directly off firm subsoil or built on a bed of natural stones. The brick foundation was built in steps as illustrated in Fig. 2. A brick foundation is little used today in this country.

The width of a concrete strip foundation depends on the bearing capacity of the subsoil and the load on the foundations. The greater the bearing capacity of the subsoil the less the width of the foundation for the same load. The minimum width of a strip foundation is 450 which gives a reasonable bearing area for most two storey houses on most subsoils and provides space in the trench to lay foundation brickwork. The least thickness of concrete for a strip foundation is generally 150 and the concrete should be at least as thick as the projection of the strip each side of the wall as illustrated in Fig. 3, where the concrete is not reinforced.

The thickness of the concrete should be not less than the projection of the strip each side of the wall as if there were a failure of the concrete by shear, the 45 degree angle of shear would not reduce the bearing of the base on the subsoil as illustrated in Fig. 4. The practical minimum depth of a strip foundation is usually 450 to allow for the removal of top soil and variations in ground level.

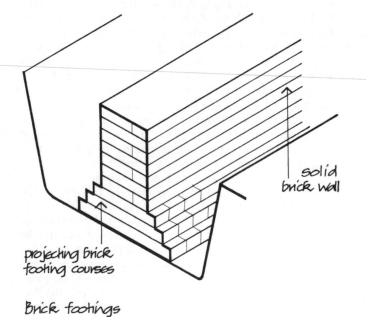

solid brick wall

projecting brick footing courses

Brick footings

Fig. 2

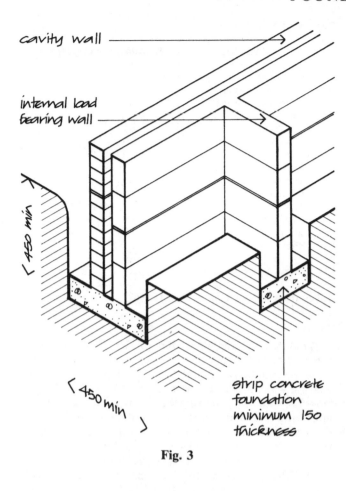

Fig. 3

cavity wall

internal load bearing wall

450 min

450 min

strip concrete foundation minimum 150 thickness

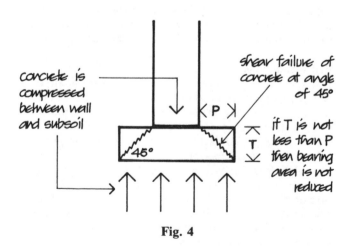

Fig. 4

concrete is compressed between wall and subsoil

45°

shear failure of concrete at angle of 45°

P

T

if T is not less than P then bearing area is not reduced

Narrow strip (trench fill) foundations: Where the bearing capacity of the subsoil and the load on the foundations require the strip to be no wider or little wider than the thickness of the wall yet the nature of the subsoil such as clay requires a depth of 0.9 m, it is usual to excavate foundation trenches and fill them with concrete up to

a level just below the finished ground level as illustrated in Fig. 5. It is cheaper to fill the trenches with concrete than excavate a wider trench to provide room for building the wall below ground. These narrow trench fill foundations are commonly excavated by machine.

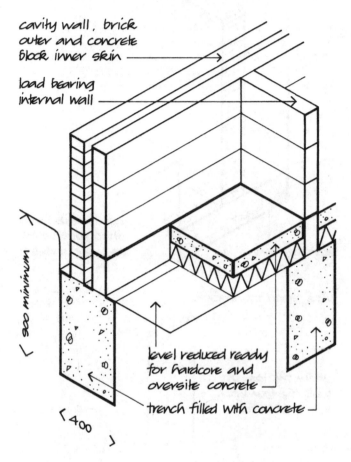

cavity wall, brick outer and concrete block inner skin

load bearing internal wall

300 minimum

level reduced ready for hardcore and oversite concrete

trench filled with concrete

400

Narrow trench fill foundation

Fig. 5

Wide strip foundations: Where the loads on foundations are considerable in relation to the bearing capacity of the subsoil, it is necessary to use a wide strip foundation to spread the load. Rather than make the thickness of the strip of concrete equal to the projection of the strip each side of the wall, it is generally cheaper to reinforce the concrete strip to reduce its thickness as illustrated in Fig. 6. Concrete is strong in compression and weak in tension and the steel reinforcement is placed in the concrete strip where tensile stress is greatest. Under load the concrete strip will tend to bend as shown in Fig. 7 and the reinforcement is therefore cast into the underside of the strip.

The Building Regulations 1976 provide a table giving the minimum width of concrete strip foundation required for various soils and loads on foundations as set out in table 3 on page 4.

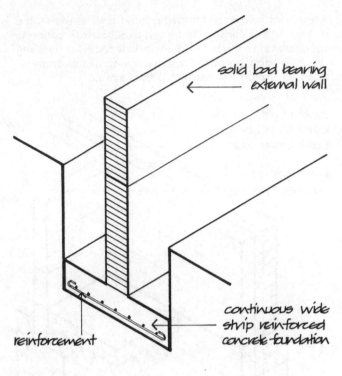

solid load bearing external wall

reinforcement

continuous wide strip reinforced concrete foundation

Wide strip foundation

Fig. 6

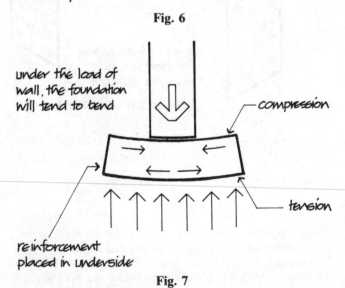

under the load of wall, the foundation will tend to bend

compression

tension

reinforcement placed in underside

Fig. 7

Loads on foundation

The load on the foundation is the accumulation of the dead loads, imposed loads and wind load.

The dead load is the force due to the static weight of all walls, partitions, floors, roofs and finishes and all other permanent construction. The unit weights of building materials is set out in BS 648.

Imposed load is the load assumed to be produced by the intended use of the building, including distributed, concentrated, impact, inertia and snow loads but excluding wind loads. Some common distributed loads are set out in table 4.

Table 4 Loading

Use of building	Distributed load (kN/m²)
Assembly buildings	
with fixed seats	4.0
without fixed seats	5.0
Bedrooms	
domestic	1.5
hotels	2.0
Boiler rooms	7.5
Bungalows	1.5
Class rooms	3.0
Dwellings	1.5
Factories	5.0; 7.0 or 10.0
Hospitals	2.0
Laboratories	3.0
Offices	
general	2.5
filing and storage	5.0

Taken from CP 3: Chap. V: Part 1: 1967

Wind load is the load due to the effects of wind pressure or suction.

In the calculation of loads on foundations for load-bearing walls it is usual to calculate the load per metre length of wall by calculating the sum of the dead, imposed and wind loads per metre of wall and from this to determine the required width of strip foundation from the type of soil on which the foundation is to bear. In the table from The Building Regulations (table 3, on page 4) the required width of foundations for given loads and soils are shown. In small buildings, such as houses, where the loads are small it is usual to assume a uniform spread of loads along walls so that a calculation of load on a metre run of wall between windows may be taken to select the width of foundation for the whole wall.

Pad foundations

It is sometimes economical to construct a foundation of isolated piers or columns of brick or concrete supporting reinforced concrete ground beams, in turn supporting walls, rather than excavating deep trenches and raising walls off strip foundations, some depth below ground. Where the subsoil has poor bearing capacity for some depth below the surface, as for example where the ground has been made up, it is often economical to use a foundation of piers on pad foundations, as illustrated in Fig. 8. The isolated concrete pad foundations are spread in the base of excavations, on which piers or columns of brick or concrete are raised to ground level to support reinforced concrete ground beams off which the walls are raised. The spread of the pad foundation is determined by the loads on it and the bearing capacity of the subsoil, and the thickness of the concrete is either at least equal to the projection of the pad each side of the pier or the pad foundation is reinforced. The spacing of the piers or columns is determined by the most economical construction.

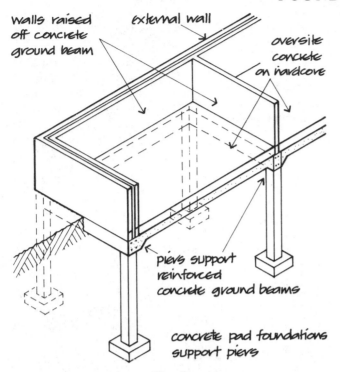

Fig. 8

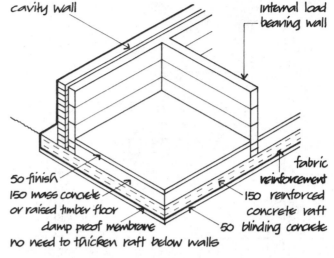

Fig. 9

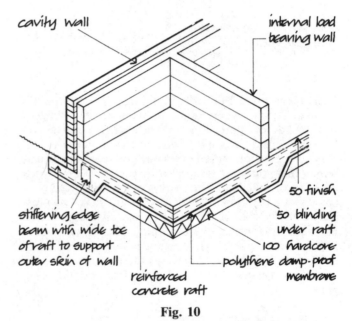

Fig. 10

Raft foundations

Raft foundations consist of a raft of reinforced concrete under the whole of the building designed to transmit the load of the building to the subsoil below the raft. Raft foundations are used for buildings on compressible ground such as very soft clays, alluvial deposits and compressible fill material where strip foundations would not provide a stable foundation.

The two types of raft commonly used are the flat raft and the wide toe raft foundation as illustrated in Figs 9 and 10. The flat slab raft is cast on a bed of blinding concrete and a moisture-proof membrane to prevent damp rising through the slab. As will be seen from Fig. 9, the slab is reinforced top and bottom and is of uniform thickness. Where the ground has a reasonable bearing capacity the raft may not need to be reinforced. For small buildings, such as two storey houses, there is no need to thicken the raft either under the external or internal loadbearing walls.

A flat slab recommended for building in areas subject to mining subsidence is similar to the flat slab, but cast on a bed of fine granular material 150 thick so that the raft is not keyed to the ground and is therefore unaffected by horizontal ground strains.

Where the ground has poor compressibility the wide toe raft is recommended, the stiffening edge beam being designed as a toe to support the outer skin of brickwork, so that the raft is not visible (Fig. 10). The raft is strengthened with a reinforced concrete edge beam under external walls and is thickened under internal loadbearing walls. There is no structural advantage in extending the edge beam down into the ground as though it were a strip foundation nor is there any need to extend the edge beam into the ground below the frost line.

On sloping sites a raft foundation can be used either on compacted levelled fill above the natural ground line as illustrated in Fig. 11, or in steps cut into the natural ground as illustrated in Fig. 11 or as cut and fill.

Pile foundations (see also Volume 4)

Where the subsoil has poor or uncertain bearing capacity or where there is likely to be appreciable ground movement as with firm, shrinkable clay or where the foundation will be deeper than say 2 m, it is often economical to use piles.

A pile is a column of concrete either cast in or driven into the ground to transfer loads through the poor bearing soil to a more stable stratum. The piles support reinforced concrete beams off which loadbearing walls are built.

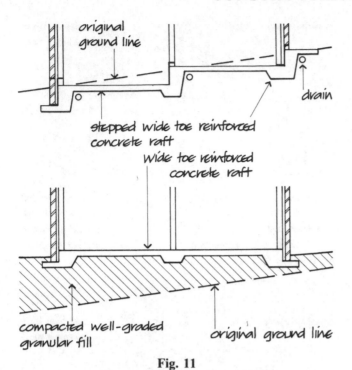

Fig. 11

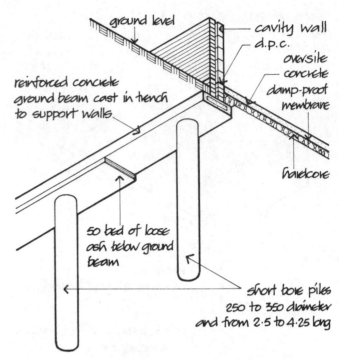

Short Bored pile foundation [worms eye view]

Fig. 12

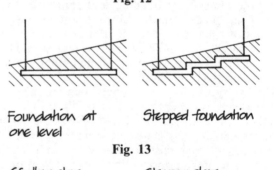

Foundation at one level   Stepped foundation

Fig. 13

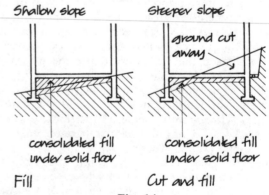

Fill   Cut and fill

Fig. 14

Short-bored piles: For small buildings, for example on shrinkable clays where adjacent trees or the felling of trees makes for appreciable volume change in the subsoil for some depth, it is often wise and economical to use a system of short-bored piles for foundations. Short-bored, that is short length, piles are cast in holes augered by hand or machine. The piles support reinforced concrete ground beams off which walls are raised as illustrated in Fig. 12. The spacing of the piles depends on the loads and the plan of the building. Piles are cast below angles and intersections of external and internal load-bearing walls and spaced between these points where the loads and the span of ground beam requires additional piles.

Foundations on sloping sites
The foundation of walls on sloping sites may be at one level or stepped as illustrated in Fig. 13.

Where the slope is slight the foundation may be at one level with the floor raised above the highest ground level. Where there is a greater slope it is usual practice to cut and fill so that the wall at the highest point does not act as a retaining wall and there is no need to raise the ground floor above the highest point of the site as illustrated in Fig. 14. The term 'cut and fill' describes the operation of cutting into part of the higher part of the site and filling the remaining lower part with excavated material or with imported fill. It will be seen that the cutting is extended beyond the wall at the highest point to provide a drained dry area behind it.

Where a building extends some distance up an appreciable slope it is usual to use stepped foundations to economise in excavation and foundation walling. The steps in the foundation should be uniform in height and equal to the thickness of the foundation concrete and be a multiple of brick courses. The steps should extend over and unite with the lower foundation not less than the thickness of the concrete foundation and in no case less than 300 as illustrated in Fig. 15.

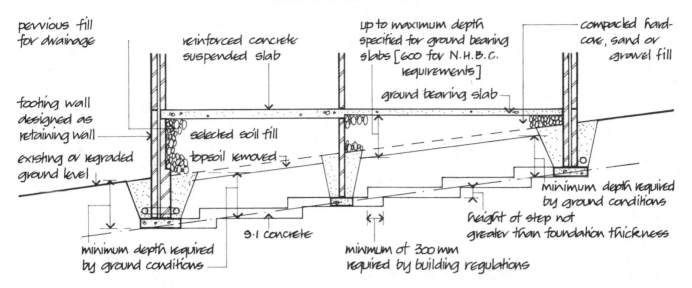

Requirements for stepped foundations   **Fig. 15**

LAND DRAINAGE

Surface water (stormwater) is the term used for natural water, that is rainwater, from the surface of the ground including open ground such as fields, paved areas and roofs. Rainwater that falls on paved areas and from roofs generally drains to surface water (stormwater) drains and thence to soakaways (see Volume 5), rivers, streams or the sea. Rainwater falling on natural open ground will in part lie on the surface of impermeable soils, evaporate to the air, run off to streams and rivers and soak into the ground. On permeable soils much of the rainwater will soak into the ground.

Ground water is that water held in soils at and below the water table (which is the depth at which there is free water below the surface). The level of the water table will vary seasonally being closest to the surface during rainy seasons and deeper during dry seasons when most evaporation to the air occurs.

Surface water (stormwater) drains
Paved areas are usually laid to falls to channels and gullies that drain to surface water drains (Volume 5).

Ground water (subsoil) drains
These are used to improve the run off of ground water to maintain the water table at some depth below the surface for the following reasons:

   (a) to improve the stability of the ground
   (b) to avoid surface flooding
   (c) to alleviate or avoid dampness in basements
   (d) to reduce humidity in the immediate vicinity of buildings.

Ground water, or land or field, drains are either open jointed or jointed, porous or perforated pipes of clayware, concrete, pitch fibres or plastic (see Volume 5). The pipes are laid in trenches to follow the fall of the ground, generally with branch drains discharging to a main drain in one of the following systems.

Natural system: The pipes are laid open jointed to follow the natural depressions and valleys of the land and connect to a main drain like tributaries to a river as illustrated in Fig. 16. This system is most used for draining open land for agriculture.

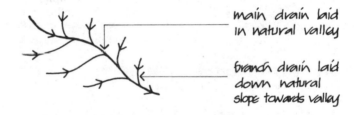

Natural system of land drains

Fig. 16

Herringbone system: The pipes are laid in a series of herringbone patterns with branches, not exceeding 30 m, discharging at an angle to a main drain that follows the fall of the land. This, more regular system, may be used with jointed pipes for land drainage around buildings, as illustrated in Fig. 17.

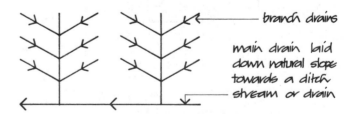

Herring bone system of land drains

Fig. 17

Grid system: Branch and main drains are laid in a regular rectangular grid with the branches connecting to one side of main drains on the boundary of the land as illustrated in Fig. 18.

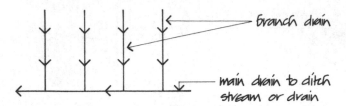

Grid system of land drains

Fig. 18

Fan shaped system: A fan of branches connect to a single main drain on the boundary of the site as illustrated in Fig. 19. This is a somewhat rough and ready system because of the difficulty of joining all the branches at one point.

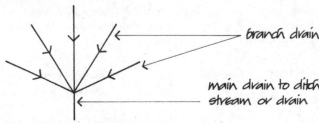

Fan shaped system of land drains

Fig. 19

Moat (cut-off) system: Drains laid on one or more sides of a building intercept the flow of ground water as illustrated in Fig. 20.

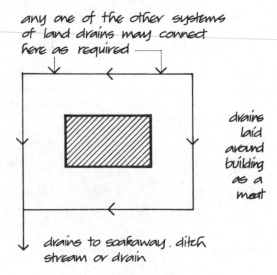

Moat or cut off system of land drains

Fig. 20

Ground water (land) drains are laid in trenches at depths of 0.6 m to 0.9 m in heavy soils and 0.9 m to 1.2 m in light soils. The nominal bore of the pipes is usually 75 and 100 for main drains and 65 or 75 for branches.

The drain trench is made wide enough to surround the pipes with clinker or is shaped, in cohesive soils, to accommodate the pipes as illustrated in Fig. 21. The pipes should be surrounded with clinker, gravel or rubble covered with inverted turf, brushwood or straw to keep fine soil from the pipes. The trench is backfilled with excavated spoil from the excavation. Where field drains are designed to collect both surface and ground water, the trench is filled with clinker, gravel or rubble to the surface as illustrated in Fig. 22.

For surface water drainage the French drain is often used. This is a trench filled with clinker, gravel or rubble as illustrated in Fig. 23.

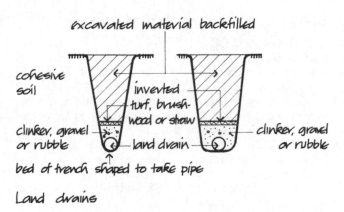

Land drains

Fig. 21

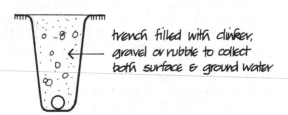

Fig. 22

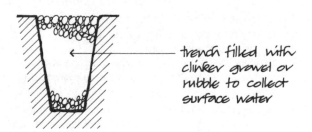

French drain

Fig. 23

CONCRETE

Concrete (see also Volume 4) is the name given to a mixture of particles of stone bound together with cement. Because the major part of concrete is of particles of broken stones and sand, it is termed the aggregate. The material which binds the aggregate is cement and this is described as the matrix.

Aggregate: The materials commonly used as the aggregate for concrete are sand and gravel. The grains of natural sand and particles of gravel are very hard and insoluble in water and can be economically dredged or dug from pits and rivers. The material dug from many pits and river beds consists of a mixture of sand and particles of gravel and is called 'ballast' or 'all-in aggregate'. The name ballast derives from the use of this material to load empty ships and barges. The term 'all-in aggregate' is used to describe the natural mixture of fine grains of sand and larger coarse particles of gravel.

All-in aggregate (ballast) is one of the cheapest materials that can be used for making concrete and was used for mass concrete work, such as large open foundations. The proportion of fine to coarse particles in an all-in aggregate cannot be varied and the proportion may vary from batch to batch so that it is not possible to control the mix and therefore the strength of concrete made with all-in aggregate. Accepted practice today is to make concrete for building from a separate mix of fine and coarse aggregate which is produced from ballast by washing, sieving and separating the fine from the coarse aggregate.

Fine aggregate is natural sand which has been washed and sieved to remove all particles larger than 5 and coarse aggregate is gravel which has been crushed, washed and sieved so that the particles vary from 5 to 6, and up to 12 to 19 in size. The fire and coarse aggregate are delivered separately. Because they have to be sieved, a prepared mixture of fine and coarse aggregate is more expensive than natural all-in aggregate. The reason for using a mixture of fine and coarse aggregate is that by combining them in the correct proportions, a concrete with very few voids or spaces in it can be made and this reduces the quantity of comparatively expensive cement required to produce a strong concrete.

Cement: The cement commonly used is ordinary Portland cement. It is manufactured by heating a mixture of finely powdered clay and limestone with water to a temperature of about 1300°C, at which the lime and clay fuse to form a clinker. This clinker is ground with the addition of a little gypsum to a fine powder of cement. Cement powder reacts with water and its composition gradually changes and the particles of cement bind together and adhere strongly to materials with which they are mixed. Cement hardens gradually after it is mixed with water. Some thirty minutes to an hour after mixing with water the cement is no longer plastic and it is said that the initial set has occurred. About ten hours after mixing with water, the cement has solidified and it increasingly hardens until some seven days after mixing with water when it is a dense solid mass.

Water-cement ratio: The materials used for making concrete are mixed with water for two reasons. Firstly to cause the reaction between cement and water which results in the cement acting as a binding agent and secondly to make the materials of concrete sufficiently plastic to be placed in position. The ratio of water to cement used in concrete affects its ultimate strength, and a certain water-cement ratio produces the best concrete. If too little water is used the concrete is so stiff that it cannot be compacted and if too much water is used the concrete does not develop full strength. The amount of water required to make concrete sufficiently plastic depends on the position in which the concrete is to be placed. The extreme examples of this are concrete for large foundations which can be mixed with comparatively little water and yet be consolidated, and concrete to be placed inside formwork for narrow reinforced concrete beams where the concrete has to be comparatively wet to be placed. In the first example, as little water is used, the proportion of cement to aggregate can be as low as say 1 part of cement to 9 of aggregate and in the second, as more water has to be used, the proportion of cement to aggregate has to be as high as say 1 part of cement to $4\frac{1}{2}$ of aggregate. As cement is expensive compared with aggregate it is usual to use as little water and therefore cement as the necessary plasticity of the concrete will allow.

Proportioning materials: The materials used for mass concrete for foundations were often measured out by volume, the amount of sand and coarse aggregate being measured in wooden boxes constructed for the purpose. This is a crude method of measuring the materials because it is laborious to have to fill boxes and then empty them into mixers and no account is taken of the amount of water in the aggregate. The amount of water in aggregate affects the finished concrete in two ways: (a) if the aggregate is very wet the mix of concrete may be too weak, have an incorrect ratio of water to cement and not develop full strength and, (b) damp sand occupies a greater volume than dry. This increase in volume of wet sand is termed bulking. The more accurate method of proportioning the materials for concrete is to measure them by weight. The materials used in reinforced concrete are commonly weighed and mixed in large concrete mixers. It is not economical for builders to employ expensive concrete mixing machinery for small buildings and the concrete for foundations, floors and lintels is usually delivered to site ready mixed, except for small batches that are mixed by hand or in a portable petrol driven mixer. The materials are measured out by volume and providing the concrete is thoroughly mixed, is not too wet and is properly consolidated the finished concrete is quite satisfactory.

Concrete mixes: British Standard 5328:1976 *Methods for specifying concrete*, gives a range of mixes. One range of concrete mixes in the Standard, ordinary prescribed mixes, is suited to general building work such as foundations and floors. These prescribed mixes should be used in place of the traditional nominal volume mixes such as 1:3:6 cement, fine and coarse aggregate by volume, that have been used in the past. The prescribed mixes, specified by dry weight of aggregate, used with 100 kg of cement, provide a more accurate method of measuring the proportion of cement to aggregate and as they are measured against the dry weight of aggregate, allow for close control of the water content and therefore the strength of the concrete.

The prescribed mixes are designated by letters and numbers as, C7P, C10P, C20P and C30P. The letter C stands for 'Compressive', the letter P for 'Prescribed' and the number indicates the 28-day characteristic cube crushing strength in newtons per square millimetre (N/mm²) which the concrete is expected to attain. The prescribed mix specifies the proportions of the mix to give an indication of the strength of the concrete sufficient for most building purposes, other than designed reinforced concrete work.

Table 5 equates the old nominal volumetric mixes of cement and aggregate with the prescribed mixes and indicates uses for these mixes.

Table 5 Concrete Mixes

Nominal volume mix	BS5328 mix	Uses
1:8 all-in 1:3:6	C7P	Foundations Site concrete
1:6 all-in 1:2½:5	C10P	Foundations Site concrete
1:2:4	C20P	Min. quality plain struc. concrete and protected reinf. concrete
1:1½:3	C30P	Reinforced concrete

Ready-mixed concrete: The very many ready-mixed concrete plants in the United Kingdom are able to supply to all but the most isolated building sites. These plants prepare carefully controlled concrete mixes which are delivered to site by lorries on which the concrete is churned to delay setting. Because of the convenience and the close control of these mixes, much of the concrete used in building today is provided by ready-mixed suppliers. To order ready-mixed concrete it is only necessary to specify the prescribed mix, for example C10P, the cement, type and size of aggregate and the workability, that is medium or high workability, depending on the ease with which the concrete can be placed and compacted.

There are water soluble sulphates in some soils, such as plastic clay, which react with ordinary cement and in time will weaken concrete. It is usual practice, therefore, to use one of the sulphate-resistant cements for concrete in contact with sulphate bearing soils.

Portland blast-furnace cement is more resistant to the destructive action of sulphates than ordinary Portland cement and is often used for concrete foundations in plastic clay subsoils. This cement is made by grinding a mixture of ordinary Portland cement with blast-furnace slag. Alternatively another type of cement known as 'sulphate resisting cement' is often used.

Sulphate resisting Portland cement: This cement has a reduced content of the aluminates that combine with soluble sulphates in some soils and is used for concrete in contact with those soils.

OVERSITE CONCRETE

Turf and top soil is removed preparatory to building operations and a hardcore bed and oversite concrete is spread as a barrier to moisture that might rise from the ground. It is practice on building sites to first build external and internal loadbearing walls from the concrete foundation up to the level of the damp-proof course, above ground, in walls. The hardcore bed and the oversite concrete are then spread and levelled within the external walls.

The Building Regulations 1976 require that a continuous layer of concrete at least 100 thick be spread over the site of all buildings within the external walls. The mix of concrete generally used is 50 kg of cement to not more than 0.1 m³ of fine aggregate and 0.2 m³ of coarse aggregate. The Building Regulations do not allow this site concrete to be laid directly on the turf or top soil of the site, but insist that all turf and other vegetable matter be removed first. The reasons for removing this vegetable soil are firstly to prevent plants, shrubs or trees from attempting to grow under the concrete. In growing, even the smallest of plant life exerts considerable pressure – which would quite quickly rupture the concrete oversite. The second reason for removing the vegetable top soil is that it readily retains moisture and would cause concrete over it to be damp at all times. The depth of vegetable top soil varies and on some sites it may be necessary to remove 300 or more vegetable top soil. If the 100 site concrete were then laid, the top surface of the concrete would be 200 below the outside ground level. The damp-proof course (d.p.c.) in all walls should be 150 above ground, so, if the top of the site concrete is 200 below ground, there will be 350 of the external walls below the d.p.c. and above the floor, making the building very liable to damp, Fig. 24.

The Building Regulations require that the top surface of the concrete 'is not below the highest level of the surface of the ground or paving adjoining any external wall of the building.'

It would of course be possible to make the site concrete 450 thick, in this instance so as to bring its top surface up to d.p.c. level, but this would be an unnecessarily expensive method. Instead, what is known as hardcore is usually spread first to raise the level of the concrete. It should be noted that it is not considered good practice

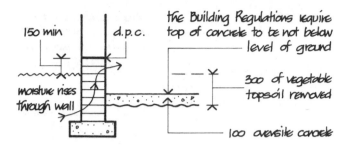

Diagram to illustrate need for hardcore
Fig. 24

to spread the soil excavated from foundation trenches over the site of buildings so as to raise the level of the site concrete, even though this would appear reasonable procedure. The excavated soil will have been broken up in digging and would need quite thorough ramming to make certain it did not sink and allow the floor to sink with it and, further, this soil would tend to retain moisture and make the site concrete damp.

Hardcore

This is the name given to the infill of materials such as broken bricks, stone or concrete, which are hard and do not readily absorb water or deteriorate. This hardcore is spread over the site within the external walls of the building to such thickness as required to raise the finished surface of the site concrete. The hardcore should be spread until it is roughly level and rammed until it forms a compact bed for the oversite concrete. This hardcore bed is usually from 100 to 300 thick.

The hardcore bed serves as a solid working base for building and as a bed for the concrete oversite. If the materials of the hardcore are hard and irregular in shape they will not be a ready path for moisture to rise by capillarity. Materials for hardcore should, therefore, be clean and free from old plaster or clay which in contact with broken brick or gravel would present a ready narrow capillary path for moisture to rise.

The materials used for hardcore should be chemically inert and not appreciably affected by water. Some materials used for hardcore, for example colliery spoil, contain soluble sulphate that in combination with water combine with cement and cause concrete to disintegrate. Other materials such as shale may expand and cause lifting and cracking of concrete. A method of testing materials for soluble sulphate is described in *Building Research Station* (*BRS*) *Digest 174*.

The materials used for hardcore are:

Brick or tile rubble: Clean, hard broken brick or tile is an excellent material for hardcore. Bricks should be free of plaster. On wet sites the bricks should not contain appreciable amounts of soluble sulphate.

Concrete rubble: Clean, broken, well-graded concrete is another excellent material for hardcore. The concrete should be free from plaster and other building materials.

Gravel and crushed hard rock: Clean, well-graded gravel or crushed hard rock are both excellent, but somewhat expensive materials for hardcore.

Chalk: Broken chalk is a good material for hardcore providing it is protected from expansion due to frost. Once the site concrete is laid it is unlikely to be affected by frost.

Pulverised fuel ash (PVA) or flyash: The fine waste material from coalburning power stations is a good material for hardcore.

Blast-furnace slag from the making of iron is a strong material which is used as hardcore.

Colliery spoil is used as a material for hardcore. Unburnt colliery spoil is preferable to burnt spoil as the former has a lower soluble sulphate content.

Before the concrete is laid it is usual to blind the top surface of the hardcore. The purpose of this is to prevent the wet concrete running down between the lumps of broken brick or stone, as this would make it easier for water to seep up through the hardcore and would be wasteful of concrete. To blind, or seal, the top surface of the hardcore a thin layer of very dry coarse concrete can be spread over it, or a thin layer of coarse clinker or ash can be used. This blinding layer, or coat, will be about 50 thick, and on it the site concrete is spread and finished with a true level top surface. Figure 25 is an illustration of hardcore, blinding and concrete oversite. Even with a good hardcore bed below the site concrete a dense hard floor finish, such as tiles, may be slightly damp in winter and will be cold underfoot. To reduce the coldness experienced with some solid ground floor finishes it is good practice to form a continuous damp-proof membrane in the site concrete.

Damp-proof membrane

The Model Health Byelaws 1936 required concrete oversite as a barrier to moisture rising from the ground. Concrete is to some degree permeable to water and will absorb moisture from the ground. A damp oversite concrete slab will be cold and draw appreciable heat from rooms if it is to be maintained at an equable temperature.

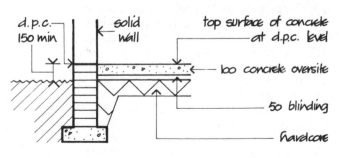

Fig. 25

A damp oversite concrete slab may cause damage and deterioration in moisture-sensitive floor finishes such as wood. On building sites that retain moisture due to a high water table and on sloping sites where water may run down to the building and wherever the site concrete is likely to be damp, it is good practice to use a damp-proof membrane under, in or on the site concrete. The Building Regulations 1976 require a damp-proof membrane in all oversite concrete slabs where this concrete incorporates timber.

A damp-proof membrane should be impermeable to water either in liquid or vapour form, be continuous with the d.p.c. in adjoining walls and be tough enough to withstand possible damage during the laying of screeds or floor finishes. The damp-proof membrane may be on top, sandwiched in or under the concrete slab.

Being impermeable to water the membrane will delay the drying out of wet concrete or screed to ground if it is under the concrete or to the lower layer of concrete if it is sandwiched in the concrete.

Surface damp-proof membranes: Floor finishes such as pitch mastic and mastic asphalt that are impermeable to water act as a combined damp-proof membrane and floor finish as illustrated in Fig. 26. Adhesives of hot soft bitumen or coal tar pitch in a continuous layer for wood block floor finishes serve as an effective surface membrane.

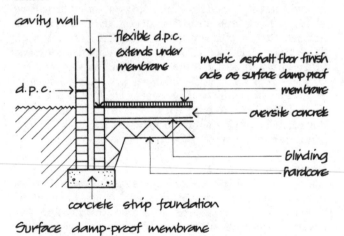

Surface damp-proof membrane

Fig. 26

Sandwich membranes used below a floor screed: Where neither the floor finish itself nor the adhesive for a floor finish acts as a damp-proof membrane and where ground conditions are likely to cause appreciable dampness in the concrete slab, it is usual today to introduce a damp-proof membrane sandwiched between the concrete oversite and the screed as illustrated in Fig. 27, or in the concrete where there is no screed. A sandwich membrane will delay wet screed or wet concrete over it drying out to the concrete below and will prevent adhesion of the screed or concrete to the surface below. The screed or top layer of concrete should be at least 50 thick to minimise the possibility of folding, due to unrestrained shrink-

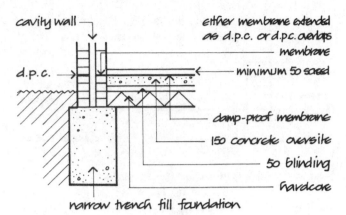

Sandwich damp-proof membrane

Fig. 27

age. A screed or concrete layer on a sandwich membrane will take a month for each 25 of its thickness to dry out sufficiently for the laying of floor finishes.

Damp-proof membrane below site concrete: On sites where the ground is persistently wet or damp, at or close to the surface, and also when under-floor heating is used, it may be advantageous to use a damp-proof membrane under the site concrete. The membrane is laid or spread on a blinding of comparatively dry concrete spread over the hardcore as illustrated in Fig. 28. These damp-proof membranes will delay the drying out of concrete to the extent of one month for each 25 thickness of concrete.

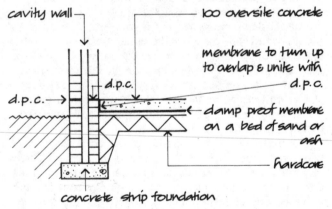

Below site concrete damp-proof membrane

Fig. 28

Materials for damp-proof membranes

Hot pitch or bitumen: A continuous layer of hot applied coal tar pitch or soft bitumen is poured on the surface and spread to a thickness of not less than 3. In dry weather, concrete is ready for the membrane three days after placing concrete. The surface of the concrete should be brushed to remove dust and primed with a solution of coal tar pitch or bitumen solution or emulsion. The pitch is heated to 35°C to 45°C and the bitumen to 50°C to 55°C.

Bitumen solution, bitumen/rubber emulsion or tar/rubber emulsion: These cold applied solutions are brushed on to the surface of concrete in three coats to a finished thickness of not less than 2.5 mm, allowing each coat to harden before the next is applied.

Mastic asphalt or pitch mastic: These materials are spread hot and finished to a thickness of at least 12.5 mm. This expensive damp-proof membrane is used where there is appreciable water pressure under the floor.

Polythene and polyethylene sheet: Polythene and polyethylene sheet is used as a damp-proof membrane with oversite concrete for all but severe conditions of dampness. It is recommended that the sheet should be at least 0.25 mm thick (1000 gauge) to avoid damage during installation. Many suppliers recommend a thickness of 0.3 mm (1200 gauge). The sheet is supplied in rolls 4 m wide by 25 m long. When used as a sandwich membrane the sheet should be laid on a blinding layer of sand or compacted fuel ash spread over the hardcore to a thickness of 12.

The sheets are spread over the blinding and lapped 150 at joints and continued across surrounding walls, under the d.p.c., for the thickness of the wall.

Where site conditions are reasonably dry and clean, the overlap joints between the sheets are sealed with mastic or mastic tape between the overlapping sheets and the joint completed with a polythene jointing tape as illustrated in Fig. 30.

Where site conditions are too wet to use mastic and tape, the joint is made by welting the overlapping sheets with a double welted fold as illustrated in Fig. 30, and this fold is kept in place by weighing it down with bricks or securing it with tape until the screed or concrete has been placed.

Where the level of the membrane is below that of the d.p.c., in adjacent walls, the sheet is dressed up against the adjacent walls and then continued over the walls below the d.p.c., as illustrated in Fig. 29.

Provided it is protected against damage during laying, subsequent building operations and in the spreading or laying of screed or concrete, these sheets act as a very effective and economical barrier against rising damp.

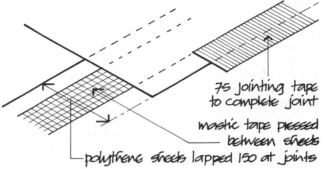

Jointing laps in polythene sheet

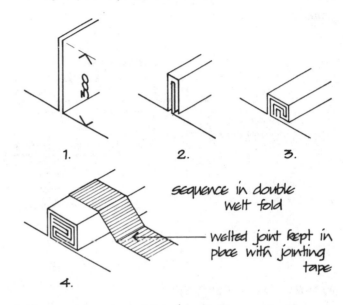

Double welted fold joint in polythene sheet

Fig. 30

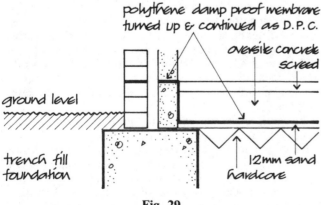

Fig. 29

Bitumen sheet: Sheets of bitumen with hessian, fibre or asbestos base are spread on the concrete oversite or on a blinding of stiff concrete below the concrete, in a single layer with the joints between adjacent sheets lapped 75. The joints are then sealed with a gas torch which melts the bitumen in the overlap of the sheets sufficient to bond them together. Alternatively the lap is made with hot bitumen spread between the overlap of the sheets which are then pressed together to make a damp-proof joint. The bonded sheets may be carried across adjacent walls as a d.p.c., or up against the walls and then across as d.p.c., where the membrane and d.p.c. are at different levels.

Bitumen sheets are fairly readily damaged on building sites and should be covered for protection as soon as possible by the screed or site concrete. Bitumen sheet is not much used as a damp-proof membrane.

Thermal insulation: There are no requirements in The Building Regulations for thermal insulation of solid ground floors. With the increasing cost of fuel it seems sensible to insulate a ground floor against loss of heat to the ground. Much of the heat loss will be through the floor adjacent to external walls so that some perimeter insulation may suffice. This can take the form of rigid insulating boards under the concrete oversite extending a metre from the external walls as illustrated in Fig. 31. It will be seen that the damp-proof membrane extends under the insulating board to prevent damp penetrating the board. Raised timber ground floors are ventilated to the open air and it is good practice to fix insulating boards under the board or chipboard floor surface to conserve heat.

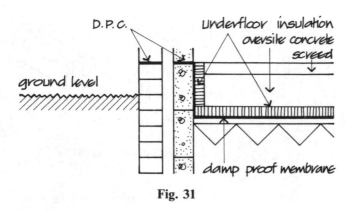

Fig. 31

DAMP-PROOF COURSES

The function of a damp-proof course is to act as a barrier to the passage of moisture or water between the parts separated by the damp-proof course. The movement of moisture or water may be upwards in the foundation of walls and ground floors, downwards in parapets and chimneys or horizontal where a cavity wall is closed at the jambs of openings.

Damp-proof courses above ground

There should be a continuous horizontal damp-proof course above ground in walls whose foundations are below ground, to prevent moisture from the ground rising through the foundation to the wall above ground, which otherwise would make wall surfaces damp and damage wall finishes. The damp-proof course above ground should be continuous for the whole length and thickness of the wall and be at least 150 above finished ground level.

It is convenient to group the materials used for damp-proof courses as flexible, semi-rigid and rigid. Flexible materials such as metal, bitumen and polythene sheet can accommodate moderate settlement movement in a building which may fracture the semi-rigid material mastic asphalt and probably fracture the rigid materials brick and slate.

Materials for damp-proof courses above ground

Flexible d.p.c.'s

Lead for use as a d.p.c. should weigh not less than 19.5 kg/m² (Code No. 4.1, 80 mm thickness). Lead is an effective barrier to moisture and water. It is liable to corrosion in contact with freshly laid lime or cement mortar and should be protected by a coating of bitumen or bitumen paint applied to the mortar surface and both surfaces of the lead. Lead is durable and flexible and can suffer distortion due to moderate settlement in walls without damage. Lead is an expensive material and is little used today other than for ashlar stonework. Lead should be laid in rolls the full thickness of the wall or leaf of cavity walls and be lapped at joints along the length of the wall and at intersections at least 100 or the width of the d.p.c.

Copper as a d.p.c. should be annealed at least 0.25 mm thick and have a nominal weight of 2.28 kg/m². Copper is an effective barrier to moisture and water, it is flexible, has high tensile strength and can suffer distortion due to moderate settlement in a wall without damage. It is an expensive material and is little used today as a d.p.c. above ground. When used as a d.p.c., it may cause staining of wall surfaces due to the oxide that forms. It is spread on an even bed of mortar and lapped at least 100 or the width of the d.p.c. at running joints and intersections.

Bitumen d.p.c.: There are seven types of bitumen d.p.c., as follows:

    (a) bitumen damp-proof course with hessian base
    (b) bitumen damp-proof course with fibre base
    (c) bitumen damp-proof course with asbestos base
    (d) bitumen damp-proof course with hessian base and lead
    (e) bitumen damp-proof course with fibre base and lead
    (f) bitumen damp-proof course with asbestos base and lead
    (g) bitumen damp-proof course with hessian base.

Bitumen d.p.c.'s are flexible and can withstand distortion due to moderate settlement in walls without damage. They may extrude under heavy loads without affecting their efficiency as a barrier to moisture. Bitumen d.p.c.'s, which are made in rolls to suit the thickness of walls, are bedded on a level bed of mortar and lapped at least 100 or the width of the d.p.c. at running joints and intersections.

Bitumen is the material most used for d.p.c.'s today because it is at once economical, flexible, reasonably durable and convenient to lay. There is nothing to choose between the three bases, hessian, fibre or asbestos as a base for a bitumen d.p.c. above ground. In moderate conditions of damp any one of the three types (a), (b) or (c) is adequate and in more severe conditions of moisture or water any one of the three lead cored types (d), (e) or (f) should be used. The lead cored d.p.c., with a lead strip weighing not less than 1.20 kg/m², joined with soldered joints, is more expensive than the bitumen alone types. In moderate to severe conditions of damp and for heavy walls, the heavier bitumen and hessian based d.p.c., (g), may be used.

Polythene sheet for use as a d.p.c. should be black low density polythene sheet of single thickness not less than 0.46 mm weighing approximately 0.48 kg/m². Polythene sheet is flexible, can withstand distortion due to moderate settlement in a wall without damage and is an effective barrier against moisture. It is laid on an even bed of mortar and lapped at least the width of the d.p.c. at running joints and intersections. Being a thin sheet material, polythene makes a thinner mortar joint than a bitumen d.p.c., and is often preferred for that reason.

Semi-rigid d.p.c.'s

Mastic asphalt spread hot in one coat to a thickness of 13 is a semi-rigid d.p.c., impervious to moisture and water. Moderate settlement in a wall may well cause a crack in the asphalt through which moisture or water may penetrate. It is an expensive form of d.p.c., which shows on the face of walls as a thick joint and it is little used as a d.p.c.

Rigid d.p.c.'s

Slates: Two courses of slates laid breaking joint in cement mortar were used as a d.p.c. before the introduction of bitumen as a d.p.c. A slate d.p.c. is little used today because of its comparatively high cost, the thick joint formed by the slates and mortar and the rigidity of the material that cannot accommodate moderate settlement in a wall without fracture.

Two courses of slates at least 230 long were laid, breaking joint in cement mortar as illustrated in Fig. 32.

Bricks: Two or three courses of dense engineering bricks laid in cement mortar serve as an effective barrier to moisture. This type of rigid d.p.c. is little used today because it is comparatively costly.

Damp-proof courses above ground should be at least 150 above the highest point of finished ground level to avoid the possibility of a build-up of material against the wall acting as a bridge for moisture from the ground as illustrated in Fig. 33.

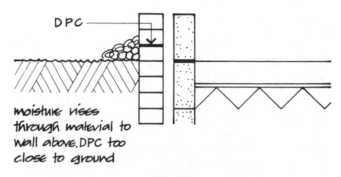

moisture rises through material to wall above. DPC too close to ground

Fig. 33

All damp-proof courses above ground must extend the full width of the wall or the leaves of cavity walls and the edges of the d.p.c.'s must not be covered with mortar, pointing or rendering.

A damp-proof course in external walls should unite with the damp-proof membrane in, on or under the over-site concrete. This may be effected either by laying the membrane in the concrete at the same level as the d.p.c. in the wall or by uniting membrane and d.p.c., laid at different levels with a vertical d.p.c., as illustrated in Fig. 31. The vertical d.p.c. or membrane involves additional site labour and is difficult to make watertight at angles and intersections. In a cavity wall the d.p.c. in the inner leaf may be at a different level to that in the outer leaf so that it is level with the membrane in the oversite concrete as illustrated in Fig. 34.

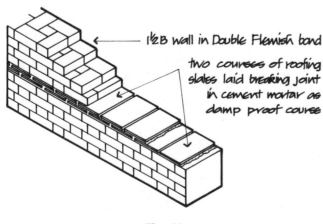

← 1½B wall in Double Flemish bond

two courses of roofing slates laid breaking joint in cement mortar as damp proof course

Fig. 32

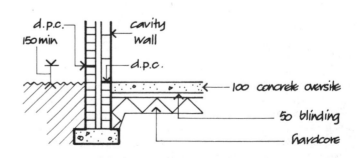

d.p.c.
150 min
cavity wall
d.p.c.
100 concrete oversite
50 blinding
hardcore

Fig. 34

EXCAVATION

The trenches which have to be dug for the foundations of walls are usually excavated by hand for single small buildings but where several houses are being built at the same time it is often economical to use mechanical trench diggers.

If the trenches are of any depth it may be necessary to erect temporary timber supports to stop the sides of the trench from falling in. The nature of the soils being excavated mainly determines the depth of trench for which timber supports to the sides should be used. Soft granular soils readily crumble and the sides of trenches in such soil may have to be supported for the full depth of the trench. The sides of trenches in clay soil do not usually require support for some depth, say up to 1.5, particularly in dry weather. In rainy weather if the bottom of the trench in clay soil gets filled with water, the water may wash out the clay from the sides at the bottom of the trench and then the whole of the sides above cave in. The purpose of temporary timbering supports to trenches is to uphold the sides of the excavation as necessary so as to avoid collapse of the sides which may endanger the lives of those working in the trench and to avoid the wasteful labour of constantly clearing falling earth from the trench bottoms. Whatever timbering is used there should be as few struts, that is horizontal members, fixed across the width of the trench as possible as these obstruct ease of working in the trench. All struts must be firmly secured so that they are not easily knocked out of position. The sides of deep trenches in compact soils such as clay should if necessary be timbered as shown in Fig. 35.

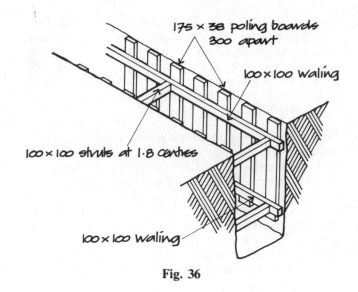

Fig. 36

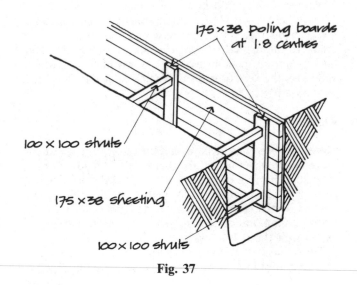

Fig. 37

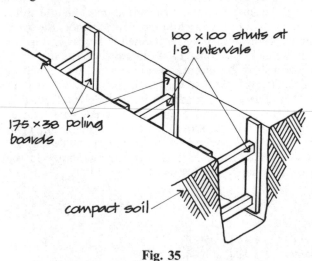

Fig. 35

If the soil is soft, such as loam, more closely spaced timbering of the sides will be needed as shown in Fig. 36.

Dry granular soils such as sand and made-up ground may need closely spaced timbering to the sides (see Fig. 37).

The sizes of timbers shown in the drawings are for guidance only, as it is impossible to set out exact rules for determining the size of timbers required.

CHAPTER TWO

WALLS

A wall is a continuous, usually vertical, solid structure of brick, stone, concrete, timber or metal, thin in proportion to its length and height, which encloses and protects a building or serves to divide buildings into compartments or rooms.

Walls are defined as external or internal to differentiate functional requirements, and as loadbearing or non-loadbearing to differentiate structural requirements.

Loadbearing walls are those that carry imposed loads, such as floors and roofs, in addition to their own weight, and non-loadbearing, those that carry only their own weight. The word partition may be used to describe any continuous structure that divides rooms or compartments. In practice, the word partition is generally used to describe a non-loadbearing internal dividing wall.

Walls are of two types, solid or framed. A solid wall (sometimes called a masonry wall) is constructed either of blocks of brick, burned clay, stone or concrete laid in mortar with the blocks laid to overlap in some form of what is called bonding or as a monolith, that is, one solid uninterrupted material such as concrete which is poured wet and hardens into a solid monolith (one piece of stone). A solid wall of blocks may be termed a block (or masonry) wall, and a continuous solid wall of concrete, a monolithic wall. A frame wall is constructed from a frame of small sections of timber, concrete or metal joined together to provide strength and rigidity, over both sides of which, or between the members of the frame are fixed thin panels of some material to fulfill the functional requirements of the particular wall. Figure 38 is an illustration of the two types of wall.

Each of the two types of wall may serve as internal or external wall and as loadbearing or non-loadbearing wall. Each of the two types of wall has different characteristics in fulfilling the functional requirements of a wall so that one type may have good resistance to fire but be a poor insulator against transfer of heat, and the other poor resistance to rain penetration yet good insulation against transfer of heat. There is no one material or type of wall that will fulfill all the functional requirements of a wall with maximum efficiency.

The traditional building was built as a box of solid walls with openings for windows and doors in the form of detached, semi-detached or a terrace of houses, for example, as illustrated in Fig. 39. The solid block walls served as protection against wind and rain, to support floors and roofs and to some extent to contain heat within the building.

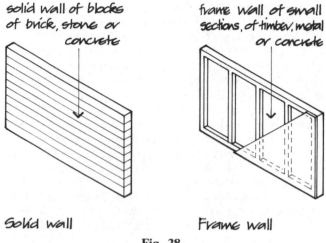

Solid wall of blocks of brick, stone or concrete

frame wall of small sections, of timber, metal or concrete

Solid wall   Frame wall

Fig. 38

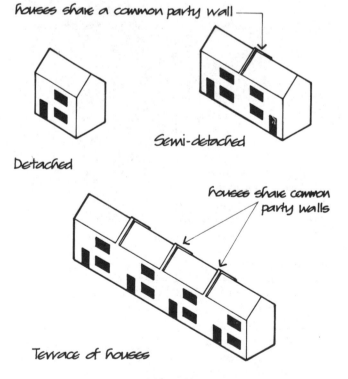

houses share a common party wall

Detached   Semi-detached

houses share common party walls

Terrace of houses

Fig. 39

The expectation of improved thermal comfort in buildings, the need to conserve natural sources of energy and the recent sharp increase in the cost of fuels has led to the need for improved insulation against loss of heat. The requirements, in The Building Regulations 1976, against heat loss can no longer be met by the conventional cavity wall of brick and concrete block skins so that another material has to be introduced.

Floors and roofs in most buildings span in one direction and require support from two opposite walls, the other walls being effectively non-loadbearing. The cross wall form of construction in terrace housing, for example, utilises the separating walls as loadbearing with some form of non-loadbearing wall at the front and the back of each house, such as a timber frame, to provide resistance to wind and rain and insulation against loss of heat. This simple building form, illustrated in Fig. 40, combines the advantages of the solid block separating wall as loadbearing and as barrier to fire and sound with the lightweight advantages of the timber frame wall to act as insulator against loss of heat and weather resistance.

In North America and recently in Britain the advantages of the solid block wall and the frame wall have been combined in the form of an outer skin of blocks and an inner skin of timber framing, where the block wall serves as protection against weather and is used for appearance sake and the inner timber skin acts as loadbearing and insulating wall.

Stability: The stability of a wall may be affected by foundation movement (see chapter 1), eccentric loads, lateral forces (wind) and expansion due to temperature and moisture changes. Eccentric loads, that is those not acting on the centre of the thickness of the wall, such as from floors, tend to overturn the wall, where the wall material, such as brick, is weak in tension. The greater the eccentricity of the load and the more slender the wall, the greater the tendency to bow. The Building Regulations 1976 and Codes of Practice set maximum height-to-thickness ratios (slenderness ratios) for walls to provide adequate thickness and stiffness against eccentric loads and lateral forces such as wind. These height-to-thickness ratios are determined by the effective height of a wall, which is either the actual height of a freestanding wall in relation to its thickness or the effective height of a wall laterally restrained against overturning by floors or roofs built into it and anchored to the wall as illustrated in Fig. 67.

Intersecting walls and piers buttress and improve the stability of straight walls against overturning and irregular profile walls have greater stability than straight walls, as illustrated in Figs 41 and 65, because of the buttressing effect of the angle of the zig-zag, chevron or serpentine wall. The smaller the angle of the zig-zag, chevron or serpentine, the greater the buttressing effect.

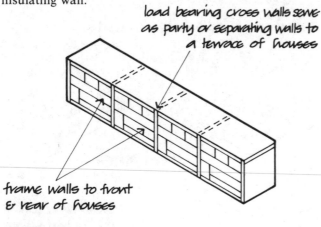

load bearing cross walls serve as party or separating walls to a terrace of houses

frame walls to front & rear of houses

Crosswall construction

Fig. 40

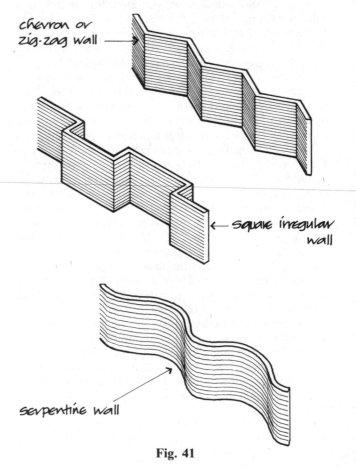

chevron or zig-zag wall

square irregular wall

serpentine wall

Fig. 41

Functional requirements
The function of a wall is to enclose and protect a building or divide space within a building. The functional requirements of a wall are:

Stability
Strength
Exclusion of rain
Durability
Fire resistance
Thermal properties
Resistance to sound transmission and sound absorption.

Walling materials may suffer expansion and contraction with temperature change and irreversible or reversible expansion with moisture change. The effect of expansion in long straight walls and walls fixed to or inside a structural frame may affect their stability where provision is not made to accommodate the expansion. Walls built of materials subject to expansion should have expansion joints along their length in long straight walls and between the wall and the frame they are fixed to or built in to, to allow for such expansion.

Strength: A wall should be designed to safely support its own weight, wind loads and the loads imposed by floors and roofs. The strength of a wall depends on the strength of the material of the wall and the wall thickness. In general, for a given material, the thicker the wall the greater the loads it can carry. The Building Regulations 1976 set out minimum thicknesses of wall in relation to height, length and loads, and these statutory thicknesses are generally adopted for small buildings as the least thickness required for strength may well be less than that required for exclusion of rain and thermal properties. For larger buildings where loadbearing walls are several storeys high it may be advantageous to make a calculation of the anticipated loads and so design the required thickness of wall to economise in materials. Walls which are designed for the actual anticipated loads are described as designed loadbearing walls or calculated walls.

Exclusion of rain: The ability of a wall to exclude wind and rain will depend to some extent on its exposure to wind. A measure of exposure is the 'driving rain index' which is a product of the annual average rainfall and the average wind speed divided by 1000. *BRS Digest 127* explains the driving rain index and contains maps showing contours of places with identical driving rain index. These maps give an indication of the average exposure to driving rain. The actual exposure of a building will depend on its site and will be affected by proximity to the coast, elevation of the site, the height of the building and proximity of other buildings all of which should be taken into account. Local experience of existing buildings should also be used as a guide to the type and thickness of wall required to exclude rain.

The behaviour of a wall in excluding wind and rain will depend on the nature of the materials used in the construction of the wall and how they are put together. A wall of facing bricks laid in a mortar will absorb an appreciable amount of the rain driven on to it so that the wall must be designed so that the rain is not absorbed to the inside face of the wall. This may be effected by making the wall of sufficient thickness, by applying an external facing of say rendering or slate hanging, or by building the wall as a cavity wall of two skins or leaves with a separating cavity.

A curtain wall of glass (see Volume 4) on the other hand will not absorb water through the impermeable sheets of glass so that driving rain will pour down the face of the glass and penetrate the joints between the

sheets of glass and the supporting frame of metal or wood so that close attention has to be made to the design of these joints that at once have to be sufficiently resilient to accommodate thermal movement and at the same time compact enough to exclude wind and rain.

It is generally accepted practice today to construct block walls of brick, stone or blocks as a cavity wall with an outer and an inner leaf or skin separated by a cavity of at least 50. The outer leaf will either be sufficiently thick to exclude rain or be protected by an outer skin of rendering or cladding of slate or tile and the inner leaf will be constructed of brick or block to support the weight of floors and roofs with either the inner leaf providing insulation against transfer of heat or the cavity filled with some thermal insulating material.

Where it is accepted that a block wall will absorb driving rain it is necessary to ensure that the rain absorbed into the wall will not adversely affect window and door frames and roof members adjacent to parapets. Damp-proof courses are built in around windows and doors and damp-proof courses and flashings in parapets to this end.

Either for the sake of appearance, or to improve resistance to penetration of driving rain, or for both reasons, the external face of walls is sometimes covered with a thin coat of rendering which is applied when the material is wet. The wet mix of sand and cement or sand, cement and lime dries and hardens to form a protective skin to the wall.

Where there is considerable exposure to driving rain, as on the coast, or as a protection to timber framed external walls, a cladding of tiles or slates is used, the slates or tiles being hung on the external face of walls.

Durability: A block wall of sound bricks, stone or blocks laid in mortar suited to the characteristics of the material, and designed with due regard to the exposure of the wall to driving rain and with sensible provision of damp-proof courses around doors and windows and to parapets, should be durable for the anticipated life of the majority of most buildings and require little if any maintenance and repair. In time, these materials exposed to wind and rain will slowly change colour. This imperceptible change will take place over many years and is described as weathering, that is a change of colour due to exposure to weather. It is generally accepted that this change, due to weathering, enhances the appearance of brick and stone walls.

Fire resistance: The resistance of the elements of a structure to collapse, flame penetration and heat transmission during a fire is expressed in periods of from one half to six hours. Various periods of resistance are called for depending on the size, nature and occupancy of the building so that the notional periods of resistance to fire of the elements of the building are assumed to be sufficient for the safe escape of occupants during fire. In general the smaller the building and the less inflammable the contents the smaller the required period of resistance to fire. In The Building Regulations 1976 are schedules of purpose-use groups of buildings and notional periods of resistance and periods of resistance for particular forms of construction.

Thermal properties: To maintain reasonable and economical conditions of thermal comfort in buildings, walls should provide adequate insulation against excessive loss or gain of heat, have adequate thermal storage capacity and the internal face of walls should be at a reasonable temperature.

For insulation against loss of heat, lightweight materials with low conductivity are more effective than dense materials with high conductivity whereas dense materials have better thermal storage capacity than lightweight materials.

Where a building is continuously heated it is of advantage to use the thermal storage capacity of a dense material on the inside face of the wall with the insulating properties of a lightweight material behind it. Here the combination of a brick or dense block inner skin, a cavity filled with some lightweight insulating material and an outer leaf of brick against penetration of rain is of advantage. Where buildings are intermittently heated it is important that inside faces of walls warm rapidly, otherwise if the inside face were to remain cold, the radiation of heat from the body to the cold wall face would make people feel cold. The rate of heating of smooth wall surfaces is improved by the use of low density, lightweight materials on or behind the inside face of walls.

Condensation is the effect of moisture from air collecting on a surface colder than the air, for example in a bathroom or kitchen where water from warm moisture-laden air condenses on to the cold surfaces of walls and glass. To minimise condensation, ventilation of the room to exchange moisture-laden air with drier outside air and good insulation of the inner face of the wall are required.

Where the material used in a wall is required to act as an insulator against transfer of heat the concern is in its capacity not as a conductor but as a resistor to transfer of heat and it is often convenient, therefore, to express its insulating property as resistivity which is the inverse of conductivity.

The loss or gain of heat through an element such as a wall is determined by its thermal transmittance or conductance which is expressed as its U value. Thermal transmittance depends on the temperature difference between the air on each side of the wall, the thermal conductance values of the materials of the wall and windows and on their relative areas. The U value is obtained from the sum of the thermal resistances of the component parts of the wall and by taking their reciprocal. Thus the thermal transmittance, or U value, is a measure of the conductance to transfer of heat, so that the higher the U value, the lower the insulation, and the lower the U value, the higher the insulation against transfer of heat.

Resistance to sound transmission and sound absorption: Sound is transmitted as airborne sound and impact sound. Airborne sound is generated as cyclical disturbances of air from, for example, a radio, that radiates from the source of the sound with diminishing intensity. Impact sound is caused by contact with a surface, as for example the slamming of a door or footsteps on a floor. The most effective insulation against airborne sound is a dense barrier such as a solid wall which absorbs the energy of the airborne sound waves. The heavier and more dense the material of the wall the more effective it is in reducing sound. The Building Regulations 1976 require walls and floors to provide sound insulation between dwellings and between machine rooms, tank rooms, refuse chutes and habitable rooms. The regulations concerning sound insulation are somewhat obscurely drawn and interpretations of them vary from one Local Authority to another. A solid wall one brick thick, or a solid cavity wall, is generally considered to provide reasonable sound reduction between dwellings at reasonable cost. The small reduction in sound transmission obtained by doubling the thickness and cost of the wall is considered prohibitive.

For reasonable reduction of airborne sound between dwellings one above the other, a concrete floor is necessary.

The more dense the material the more readily it will transmit impact sound. A knock on a part of a rigid concrete frame may be heard some considerable distance away. Insulation against impact sound will therefore consist of some absorbent material that will act to cushion the impact, such as a carpet on a floor, or serve to interrupt the path of the sound, as for example the absorbent pads under a floating floor.

Noise generated in a room may be reflected from the walls and ceilings and build up to an uncomfortable intensity inside the room particularly where the wall and ceiling surfaces are hard and smooth. To prevent the build-up of reflected sound some absorbent material should be applied to walls and ceilings, such as acoustic tiles or curtains, to absorb the energy of the sound waves.

BRICKS

The word brick is used to describe a small block of burned clay of such size that it can be conveniently held in one hand and is slightly longer than twice its width. Blocks made from sand and lime and blocks made of concrete are manufactured in clay brick size and these are also called bricks. The great majority of bricks in use today are of clay.

The standard brick is $215 \times 102.5 \times 65$ which with a 10 mortar joint becomes $225 \times 112.5 \times 75$ to BS 3921, Part 2.

BRICKS

Materials from which bricks are made

Clay: In this country there are very extensive areas of clay soil suitable for brickmaking. Clay differs quite widely in composition from place to place and the clay dug from one part of a field may well be quite different from that dug from another part of the same field. Clay is ground in mills, mixed with water to make it plastic and moulded, either by hand or machine, to the shape and size of a brick.

Bricks that are shaped and pressed by hand in a sanded wood mould and then dried and fired have a sandy texture, are irregular in shape and colour and are used as facing bricks due to the variety of their shape, colour and texture. Machine made bricks are either hydraulically pressed in steel moulds or extruded as a continuous band of clay. The continuous band of clay, the section of which is the length and width of a brick, is cut into bricks by a wire frame. Bricks made this way are called 'wire cuts'. Press moulded bricks generally have a frog or indent and wire cuts have none. The moulded brick is baked to dry out the water and burned at a high temperature so that part of the clay melts and fuses the whole mass of the brick into a hard durable unit. If the moulded brick is burned at too high a temperature part of the clay melts into a solid glass-like mass and if it is burned at too low a temperature no part of the clay melts and the brick is soft. Neither over-burned nor under-burned brick is satisfactory for building purposes.

A brick wall has very good fire resistance, is a moderately good insulator against transference of heat, does not, if well built, deteriorate structurally and requires very little maintenance over a long period of time. Bricks are cheap because there is an abundance of the natural material from which they are made, that is clay. The clay can easily be dug out of the ground, it can readily be made plastic for moulding into brick shapes and it can be burned into a hard, durable mass at a temperature which can be achieved with quite primitive equipment.

Because there is wide variation in the composition of the clays suitable for brick making and because it is possible to burn bricks over quite a wide range of temperatures sufficient to fuse the material into a durable mass, a large variety of bricks are produced in this country. The bricks produced which are suitable for building vary in colour from almost dead white to practically black and in texture from almost as smooth as glass to open coarse grained. Some are quite light in weight and others dense and heavy and there is a wide selection of colours, textures and densities between the extremes noted. It is not possible to classify bricks simply as good and bad as some are good for one purpose and not for another. Bricks may be classified in accordance with their uses as commons, facings and engineering bricks or by their quality as internal quality, ordinary quality and special quality. The use and quality classifications roughly coincide as commons are much used for internal walls, facings or ordinary quality for external walls and engineering or special quality bricks for their density and durability in positions of extreme exposure. In cost, commons are cheaper than facings and facings cheaper than engineering bricks.

Types of bricks

Commons: These are bricks which are sufficiently hard to safely carry the loads normally supported by brickwork, but because they have a dull texture or poor colour they are not in demand for use as facing bricks which show on the outside when built and affect the appearance of buildings. These 'common' bricks are used for internal walls and for rear walls which are not usually exposed to view. Any brick which is sufficiently hard and of reasonably good shape and of moderate price may be used as a 'common' brick. The type of brick most used as a common brick is the *Fletton* brick.

Facings: This is by far the widest range of bricks as it includes any brick which is sufficiently hard burned to carry normal loads, is capable of withstanding the effects of rain, wind, soot and frost without breaking up and which is thought to have a pleasant appearance. As there are as many different ideas of what is a pleasant looking brick as there are bricks produced, this is a somewhat vague classification.

Engineering bricks: These are bricks which have been made from selected clay, which have been carefully prepared by crushing, have been very heavily moulded and carefully burned so that the finished brick is very solid and hard and is capable of safely carrying much heavier loads than other types of brick. These bricks are mainly used for walls carrying exceptionally heavy loads, for brick piers and general engineering works. The two best known engineering bricks are the red Southwater brick and the blue Staffordshire brick. Both are very hard, dense and do not readily absorb water. The ultimate crushing resistance of engineering bricks is greater than 50 N/mm².

Semi-engineering bricks: These are bricks which whilst harder than most ordinary bricks are not so hard as engineering bricks. It is a very vague classification without much meaning, more particularly as a so-called semi-engineering brick which can safely carry less weight than an engineering brick is not necessarily half the price of an engineering brick.

Composition of clay: Clays suitable for brickmaking are composed mainly of silica in the form of grains of sand and alumina which is the soft plastic part of clay which readily absorbs water and makes the clay plastic and which melts when burned. Present in all clays are materials other than the two mentioned above such as lime, iron, manganese, sulphur and phosphates. The proportions of these materials varies widely and the following is a description of the composition, nature and uses of some of the most commonly used bricks classified according to the types of clay from which they are produced.

Flettons: There are extensive areas of what is known as Oxford clay. The clay is composed of just under half silica, or sand, about one-sixth alumina, one-tenth lime and small measures of other materials such as iron, potash and sulphur. The clay lies in thick beds which are economical to excavate. In the clay, in its natural state, is a small amount of mineral oil which, when the bricks are burned, ignites and assists in the burning. Because there are extensive thick beds of this clay, which are economical to excavate, and because it contains some oil, the cheapest of all clay bricks can be produced from it. The name Fletton given to these bricks derives from the name of a suburb of Peterborough around which the clay is extensively dug for brickmaking. Flettons are cheap and many hundreds of millions of them are used in building every year. The bricks are machine-moulded and burned and the finished brick is uniform in shape with sharp square edges or arises. The bricks are dense and hard and have moderately good strength, the average pressure at which these bricks fail, that is crumble, is around 21 N/mm².

The bricks are usually light creamy pink to dull red in colour and because of the smooth face of the brick what are known as 'kiss marks' are quite distinct on the long faces. These 'kiss marks' take the form of three bands of different colours, as illustrated in Fig. 42.

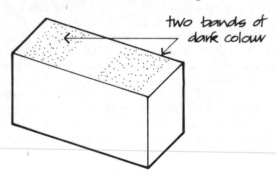

View of Fletton brick showing kiss marks on stretcher face

Fig. 42

The surface is quite hard and smooth and if the brick is to be used for wall surfaces to be plastered, two faces are usually indented with grooves to give the surface a better grip or key for plaster. The bricks are then described as 'keyed Flettons'. Figure 43 is an illustration of a keyed Fletton.

Stocks: The term 'stock brick' is generally used in the south-east counties of England to describe the London stock brick. This is a brick manufactured in Essex and Kent from clay composed of sand and alumina to which some chalk is added. Some combustible material is added to the clay to assist burning. The London stock is usually

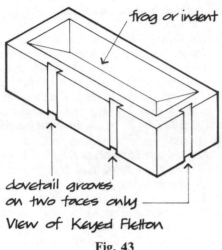

View of Keyed Fletton

Fig. 43

predominantly yellow after burning with shades of brown, and purple. The manufacturers grade the bricks as 1st Hard, 2nd Hard and Mild, depending on how hard burned they are. The bricks are usually irregular in shape and have a fine sandy texture. Because of their colour they are sometimes called 'yellow stocks'. 1st Hard and 2nd Hard London stocks are much used in and around London as facings as they weather well and are of reasonable price. In other parts of England the term stock bricks describes the stock output of any given brick field.

Marls: By origin the word marl denotes a clay containing a high proportion of lime (calcium carbonate) but by usage the word marl is taken to denote any sandy clay. This derives from the use of sandy clays, containing some lime, as a top dressing to some soils to increase fertility. In most of the counties of England there are sandy clays, known today as marls, which are suitable for brickmaking. Most of the marl clays used for brickmaking contain little or no lime. Many of the popular facing bricks produced in the Midlands are made from this type of clay and they have a good shape, a rough sandy finish and vary in colour from a very light pink to dark mottled red.

Gaults: The gault clay does in fact contain a high proportion of lime and the burned brick is usually white or pale pink in colour. These bricks are of good shape and texture and make good facing bricks, and are more than averagely strong. The gault clay beds are not extensive in this country and lie around limestone and chalk hills in Sussex and Hampshire.

Clay shale bricks: Some clay beds have been so heavily compressed over centuries by the weight of earth above them that the clay in its natural state is quite firm and has a compressed flaky nature. In the coal-mining districts of this country a considerable quantity of this clay shale has to be dug out to reach coal seams and in those districts the extracted shale is used extensively for brickmaking. The bricks produced from this shale are usually uniform in shape with smooth faces and the bricks are hard and durable. The colour of the bricks is usually dull buff, grey, brown or red. These bricks are used as facings, commons and semi-engineering, depending on their quality.

Calcium silicate bricks are generally known as sand-lime bricks. The output of these bricks has increased over the past few years principally because the output of Fletton bricks could not keep pace with the demand for a cheap common brick and sand-lime bricks have been mainly used as commons. The bricks are made from a carefully controlled mixture of clean sand and hydrated lime which is mixed together with water, heavily moulded to brick shape and then the moulded brick is hardened in a steam oven. The resulting bricks are very uniform in shape and colour and are normally a dull white. Coloured sand-lime bricks are made by adding a colouring matter during manufacture. These bricks are somewhat more expensive than Flettons and because of their uniformity in shape and colour they are not generally thought of as being a good facing brick. The advantage of them however is that the material from which they are made can be carefully selected and accurately proportioned to ensure a uniform hardness, shape and durability quite impossible with the clay used for most bricks.

Flint-lime bricks are manufactured from hydrated lime and crushed flint and are moulded and hardened as are sand-lime bricks. They are identical with sand-lime bricks in all respects.

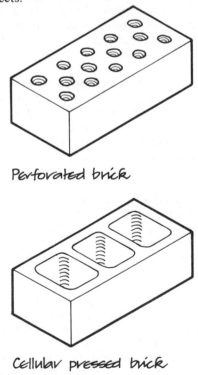

Perforated brick

Cellular pressed brick

Fig. 44

Hollow, perforated and special bricks: Cellular and perforated bricks, illustrated in Fig. 44, are lighter in weight than solid bricks and the cells and perforations facilitate drying and burning. The saving in clay and consequent reduction in weight is an advantage in non-loadbearing walls but does not significantly improve thermal insulation in external walls. Cellular bricks are laid with the cells or hollows downwards and perforated bricks should be laid so that the mortar does not fill the perforations.

The structural 'V' brick developed by the Building Research Station, was designed for use in place of the traditional cavity wall. The vertical perforations provide thermal insulation equivalent to a cavity wall. These bricks can be held in one hand and have to be carefully laid so that mortar does not enter the cavities. The structural 'V' brick is not so easy to handle as the conventional brick as its sharp edges lacerate the hands and the care required in spreading mortar makes it far less popular in use than was originally anticipated.

A range of standard special bricks, illustrated in Fig. 45, is produced for use in facing brickwork for angles, offsets and returns.

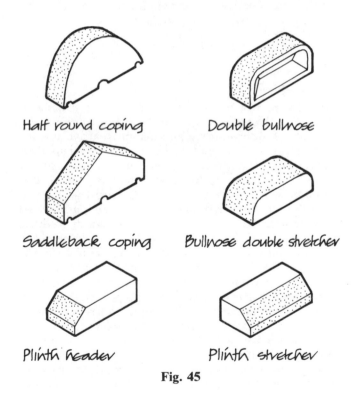

Half round coping   Double bullnose

Saddleback coping   Bullnose double stretcher

Plinth header   Plinth stretcher

Fig. 45

Properties of bricks

Hardness: This is a somewhat vague term very commonly used in the description of bricks. By general agreement it is recognised that a brick which is to have a moderately good compressive strength, reasonable resistance to saturation by rain water and sufficient resistance to the disruptive action of frost should be hard burned. Without some experience in the handling, and of the behaviour of bricks in general, it is very difficult to determine whether or not a particular brick is hard burned. A method of testing for hardness is to hold the brick in one hand and give it a light tap with a hammer. The sound caused by the blow should be a dull ringing tone and not a dull thud. Obviously different types of brick will when tapped give off different sorts of sound and a brick that gives off a dull sound when struck may well be hard burned. The student will learn much of behaviour of a particular type of brick used for different types of wall by examination of existing buildings and questioning those most experienced in the building and design of walls.

Compressive strength: This is the only property of bricks which can be determined accurately. The compressive strength of bricks is found by crushing 12 of them individually until they fail or crumble. The pressure required to crush them is noted and the average compressive strength of the brick is stated as newtons per mm² of surface area required to ultimately crush the brick. The crushing resistance varies from about 3.5 N/mm² for soft facing bricks up to 140 N/mm² for engineering bricks. The following are some comparative figures:

Mild (i.e. soft) stocks	3.5 N/mm²
2nd Hard stocks	17.5 N/mm²
Flettons	21 N/mm²
Southwater A	70 N/mm².

Absorption: Much scientific work has been done to determine the amount of water absorbed by bricks and the rate of absorption, in an attempt to arrive at some scientific basis for grading bricks according to their resistance to the penetration of rain. This work has to date been of little use to those concerned with general building work. A wall built of very hard bricks which absorb little water may well be more readily penetrated by rain water than one built of bricks which absorb a lot of water. This is because rain will more easily penetrate a small crack in the mortar between bricks if the bricks are dense than if the bricks around the mortar are absorptive. Experimental soaking in water of bricks gives a far from reliable guide to the amount of water they can absorb as air in the pores and minute holes in the brick may prevent total absorption and to find total absorption the bricks have to be boiled in water or heated. The amount of water a brick will absorb is a guide to its density and therefore its strength in resisting crushing but is not a reasonable guide to its ability to weather well in a wall. This term 'weather well' describes the ability of the bricks in a particular situation to suffer rain, frost and wind without losing strength, without crumbling and to keep their colour and texture.

Frost resistance: A very few failures of brickwork due to the disruptive action of frost have been reported during the last twenty years and scientific work has sought to determine a brick's resistance to frost failure. The few failures reported were in exposed parapet walls or chimney stacks where brickwork suffers most rain saturation and there is a likelihood of damage by frost. Few failures of ordinary brick walls below roof level have been reported and a knowledge of the resistance to frost failure seems of little importance providing sensible precautions are taken in the design of parapets and stacks above roof level and brick walls in general are protected from saturation by damaged rain-water gutters or blocked rain-water pipes.

Parapet walls, chimney stacks and garden walls should be built of sound, hard burned bricks protected with coping, cappings and damp-proof courses.

Efflorescence: Clay bricks contain soluble salts that migrate, in solution in water, to the surface of brickwork as water evaporates to outside air. These salts will collect on the face of brickwork as an efflorescence (flowering) of white crystals that appear in irregular, unsightly patches. This efflorescence of white salts is most pronounced in parapet walls, chimneys and below damp-proof course where brickwork is most liable to saturation. The concentration of salts depends on the soluble salt content of the bricks and the degree and persistence of saturation of brickwork. The efflorescence of white salts on the surface is merely unsightly and will cause no damage. In time these salts may be washed from surfaces by rain.

Crypto-efflorescence: Where the surface of the bricks is smooth and dense the soluble salts will be trapped behind the face of bricks. These salts expand and in time cause the face of bricks to crumble and disintegrate. At first the effect is unsightly. From subsequent wetting and freezing more serious disintegration may occur. Fletton bricks are particularly subject to this crypto-efflorescence.

Sulphate attack on mortars and renderings: When brickwork is persistently wet, as in foundations, retaining walls, parapets and chimneys, soluble sulphates in bricks and mortar may in time crystalise and expand and cause mortar and renderings to disintegrate. To minimise this effect bricks with a low sulphate content should be used.

Bonding

In building a wall of bricks or blocks it is usual to lay the bricks in some regular pattern so that each brick bears partly upon two or more bricks below itself. The bricks are said to be bonded, meaning they bind together by being laid across each other. The following is an explanation of the reason for bonding bricks in brickwork.

When a child is first given a set of toy bricks, his natural instinct is to pile them one on another as high as possible, Fig. 46. He soon finds however that the narrow high stack is very unstable and can easily be knocked down, but, if he arranges them in pyramid fashion, Fig. 47, the stack or wall is much less easily knocked down. If we examine the pyramid style of the child's building we see that the

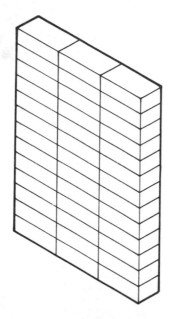

stacks of bricks with continuous
vertical joints between the stacks

Fig. 46

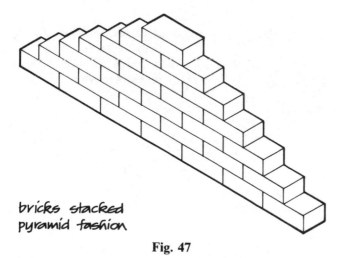

bricks stacked
pyramid fashion

Fig. 47

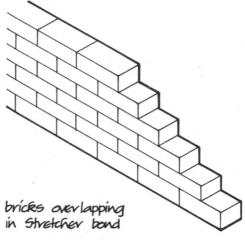

bricks overlapping
in stretcher bond

Fig. 48

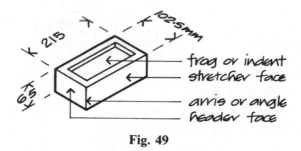

Fig. 49

bricks overlap one another, Fig. 48, and this is one kind of bond used in brickwork, namely, 'stretcher' bond. The bonding of bricks in a brick wall is an extension of the use of stone blocks in the pyramids. A wall has to carry the weight of the floors and roofs and we see from the child's experience that a bonded wall more safely carries loads, that is it is less easily over-turned than one not bonded, more particularly as the loads on a wall do not bear down vertically on the centre of the thickness of a wall. If we look back at the child's first attempt to build we see that his wall consisted of vertical stacks of bricks, next to each other, and that the wall is only as strong as one stack of bricks because if one stack collapses or even one brick is dislodged the whole wall will easily fall

down. Because the wall is made of adjacent stacks of bricks there are continuous vertical joints between each stack. It is generally accepted that continuous vertical joints of this sort in a wall of blocks or bricks is a sign of weakness.

The standard size of a brick is $215 \times 102.5 \times 65$ and for convenience in describing the arrangement of bricks in different bonds the faces of a brick have been named, Fig. 49.

There are two 'header' faces, each 102.5 mm wide and 65 deep and two 'stretcher' faces each 215 long by 65 deep. The brick is laid on one of its larger 215×102.5 mm faces, called the 'bed'. The indent or sinking shown in the sketch is termed a 'frog'. Some bricks have no indent or frog at all, some have one in one face only and some have indents in both long faces.

The indents or frogs in the bed faces of bricks vary in section. Most Flettons have a V-section indent in one face only, and Southwater engineering bricks have an indent roughly rectangular in section. The reason for forming indents in bricks is that a protruding surface on the mould used to give the brick its shape will more surely compact the wet clay than a flat surface. It has been said that the indents or frogs are formed to facilitate the bedding of bricks in mortar but as many bricks, for example those prepared by the wire cut process, have no indent or frog at all and can readily be bedded in mortar, the explanation seems somewhat specious.

Stretcher bond: A wall which is to be 102.5 mm thick is usually built with bricks overlapping or bonded as described above. The bricks are laid on bed with every brick showing a stretcher or long face on each side of the wall, hence the term stretcher bond.

Walls which have to carry heavy loads or which are required to keep out rain have to be thicker than 102.5 mm and the wall is built by laying bricks side by side to produce any required thickness which is a multiple of the width of a brick.

It has been common practice to describe the thickness of brick walls as 102.5 mm, 215, 327.5 mm, 430 and so on, which presumes that all bricks are the same size. But as bricks vary in size it is more accurate to describe the thickness of walls as $\frac{1}{2}B$, $1B$, $1\frac{1}{2}B$, $2B$ and so on, taking B as being the length of the particular brick used, which in the case of Flettons is 215.

Just as the child's wall was made more secure by overlapping the bricks or bonding them along the length of the wall, so in walls of more than 102.5 mm thickness the bricks should be bonded or overlapped into the thickness of the wall.

If a wall is to be built $1B$ thick it is possible to arrange the bricks so that every brick shows a header face on each side of the wall and the bricks along the length of the wall are bonded as shown in Fig. 50.

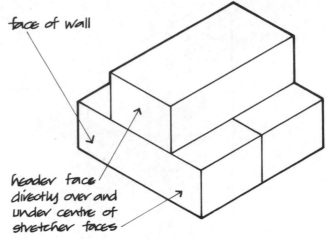

face of wall

header face directly over and under centre of stretcher faces

Basic arrangement of bricks for bonding

Fig. 51

In English bond the bricks in one course or layer show their header faces and in the course below and above their stretcher faces, as shown in Fig. 52.

In Flemish bond the bricks in every course or layer show alternately header and stretcher faces, Fig. 53.

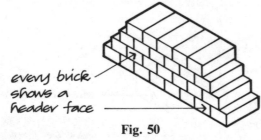

every brick shows a header face

Fig. 50

This arrangement is termed 'heading' or 'header' bond as every brick shows a header face. This type of bond is very little used for $1B$ thick walls because the general opinion is that the finished effect is not pleasing. The great number of vertical joints between the header faces of bricks usually does not look attractive.

There is only one basic method of arranging or bonding bricks to avoid every brick showing a header face and so that there are no continuous vertical joints, that is to lay the bricks so that the header face of a brick lies directly over the centre of the stretcher face of a brick in the course below and above, Fig. 51.

By trial and error the student will quickly appreciate that apart from header bond this is the only other possible basic arrangement of bonding for walls at least $1B$ thick if the bricks are to be bonded to avoid continuous vertical joints and the instability of walls with such joints.

English and Flemish bond: These are the two types of bond most commonly used and in each the arrangement just described is used, namely a header face centrally over and under a stretcher face.

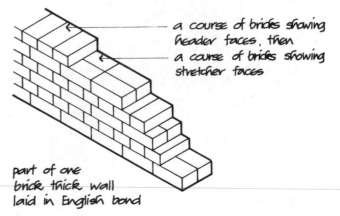

a course of bricks showing header faces, then a course of bricks showing stretcher faces

part of one brick thick wall laid in English bond

Fig. 52

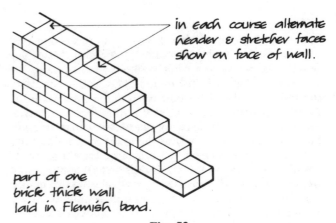

in each course alternate header & stretcher faces show on face of wall.

part of one brick thick wall laid in Flemish bond.

Fig. 53

The header face of many bricks is a darker colour than the stretcher face of the same brick, and it is generally thought that the appearance of a wall in Flemish bond is more attractive than one in English bond. In the former the darker faces are separated by the lighter coloured stretcher faces and in the latter the darker header faces lie in continuous courses.

Angles and quoins: At the end of a wall where it returns round the corner or angle of the building the arrangement of the bricks described above has to be slightly altered. If we look at the drawing of bonding (Fig. 52) we see that everywhere in the length of the wall bricks project or set back $\frac{1}{4}B$ from the bricks above or below. Obviously if the wall is to end with a straight vertical angle then in some way this $\frac{1}{4}B$ overlap must be filled in or closed. The usual method of filling in this $\frac{1}{4}B$ wide space is to utilise a brick cut in half along its length so that each half of the brick is $1B$ long by $\frac{1}{4}B$ wide by 65 deep. Because this cut brick is used to fill in or *close* the bond of the bricks it is called a 'closer' and the particular name given to this sized brick is 'queen closer'. It is not always possible to cut a brick cleanly in half and sometimes half queen closers are cut. A full closer and two half closers are shown in Fig. 54.

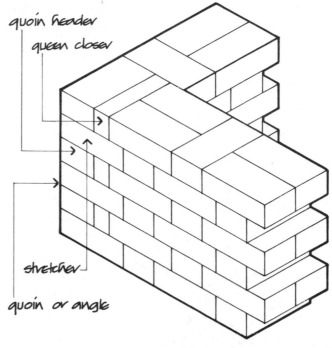

Fig. 55

The word 'quoin' derives from the French word *coin* meaning corner or angle. Figures 56 and 57 show two successive courses of brickwork for walls $1\frac{1}{2}B$ thick in Flemish and English bond. The walls are drawn showing the bonding at angles or quoins.

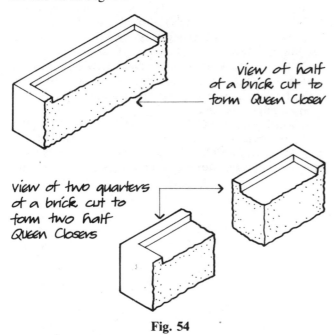

Fig. 54

The closer brick is utilised at the angles of walls as in Fig. 55. It will be noticed that the closer brick is not placed at the angle of the wall but $\frac{1}{2}B$ in from the angle next to the header face showing at the angle. The reason for this is that the narrow closer might, if placed at the angle, be easily displaced whilst the wall is being built. The rule for completing or closing the bond at angles is to place a queen closer next to the angle or quoin header in every other course of bricks and this is true irrespective of which sort of bond is used or the thickness of the wall.

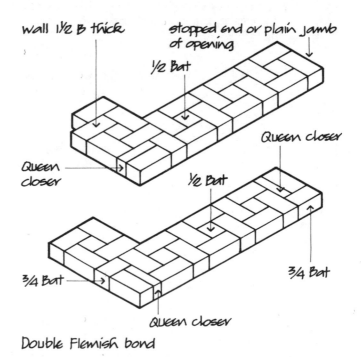

Fig. 56

31

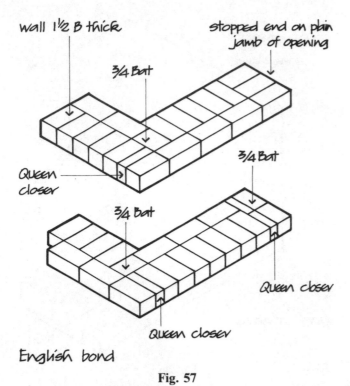

Fig. 57

Single and double Flemish bond: A wall which is $1\frac{1}{2}B$ thick and is to have the appearance on face of Flemish bond, that is with headers and stretchers alternately in each course, can be built in one of two ways. The first way is to arrange the bricks in what is called single Flemish bond so that the external face shows a Flemish bond appearance and the internal face which will be covered with plaster shows an English bond appearance. This is shown in Fig. 58.

The Flemish bond appearance on one face of the wall is achieved by cutting half bricks as shown. The reason for doing this is to economise in the use of expensive facing bricks by cutting some in half to form two header faces so that most of the inner $1B$ of the wall can be of cheaper common bricks.

The other way to build this wall is to arrange the bricks so that they show Flemish bond appearance on both faces and this would be done if the bricks were to be left unplastered on both sides of the wall. This bond, called double Flemish bond, is shown in Fig. 59 and as will be seen a number of half bricks, marked $\frac{1}{2}$ bat, have to be used. This is a wasteful method of using bricks as half brick size is not manufactured but has to be cut from a whole brick. Very rarely indeed can a whole brick be cut into two exact halves. Usually the smaller 'half' of the broken brick is thrown away. This is obviously a wasteful way of using bricks.

Garden wall bonds: Walls, such as garden walls, that are to be finished fairface both sides are often built in one of the garden wall bonds. The term, fairface, in relation to brickwork indicates that the wall face is to be exposed with a neat, flush, facing brick finish.

Because of variations in the size and shape of many facing bricks it is difficult to finish a $1B$ wall fairface both sides because of differences in the length of bricks that are bonded through the thickness of the wall and show their header faces both sides. Garden wall bonds are designed to reduce the number of header faces to facilitate a fairface finish both sides in walls where appearance is more important than stability.

It will be seen from Fig. 59 that there is one course of header bricks to every three courses of stretchers in English garden wall bond and one header to every three stretchers in each course in Flemish garden wall bond.

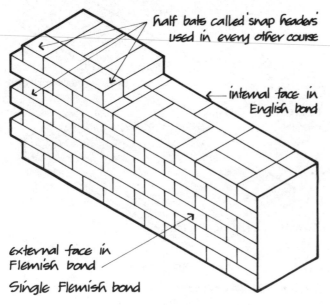

Fig. 58

Fig. 59

MORTAR FOR BRICKWORK

Clay bricks are never exactly rectangular in shape and they vary in size. Many facing bricks are far from uniform in shape and size and if a wall were built of bricks laid without mortar and the bricks were bonded the result might be as shown, exaggerated in Fig. 60.

Badly shaped facing bricks laid without mortar

Fig. 60

Because of the variations in shape and size, the courses of bricks would not lie anywhere near horizontal. One of the functions of brickwork is to support floors and if a floor timber were to bear on the brick marked A it would tend to cause it to slide down the slope on which it would be resting. It is essential therefore that brickwork be laid in true horizontal courses, and the only way this can be done with bricks of differing shapes and sizes is to lay them on some material which is sufficiently plastic whilst the bricks are being laid to take up the difference in size, and which must be able to harden to such an extent that it can carry the weight normally carried by brickwork. The material used is termed mortar. The basic requirements of a mortar are that it will harden to such an extent that it can carry the weight normally carried by bricks, without crushing, and that it be sufficiently plastic when laid to take the varying sizes of bricks. It must have a porosity similar to that of the bricks and it must not deteriorate due to the weathering action of rain or frost. Sand is a natural material which is reasonably cheap and which if mixed with water can be made plastic, yet which has very good strength in resisting crushing. Its grains are also virtually impervious to the action of rain and frost. The material required to bind the grains of sand together into a solid mass is termed the matrix and two materials used for this purpose are lime and cement.

Aggregate for mortar

Sand: The aggregate or main part of mortar is sand. The sand is dredged from pits or river beds and a good sand should consist of particles of differing sizes from dust up to 5 in size. In the ground, sand is usually found mixed with some clay earth which coats the particles of sand. If sand mixed with clay is used for mortar, the clay tends to prevent the cement or lime binding the sand particles together and in time the mortar crumbles. It is therefore important that the sand be thoroughly washed

so that there is no more than 5% of clay in the sand delivered to site.

Soft sand and sharp sand: Sand which is not washed and which contains a deal of clay in it feels soft and smooth when held in the hand, hence the term soft sand. Sand which is clean feels coarse in the hand, hence the term sharp. These are terms used by craftsmen. When soft sand is used, the mortar is very smooth and plastic and it is much easier to spread and to bed the bricks in than a mortar made of sharp or clean sand. Naturally the bricklayer prefers to use a mortar made with soft or unwashed sand. A good washed sand for mortar should, if clenched in the hand, leave no trace of yellow clay stains on the palm.

Matrix for mortar

Cement – lime: Cement is made by heating a finely ground mixture of clay and limestone, and water, to a temperature at which the clay and limestone fuse into a clinker. The clinker is ground to a fine powder called cement. The cement most commonly used is ordinary Portland cement which is delivered to the site in 50 kg sacks. When the fine cement powder is mixed with water a chemical action between water and cement takes place and at the completion of this reaction the nature of the cement has so changed that it binds itself very firmly to most materials. If the cement is thoroughly mixed with sand and water, the reaction takes place, the excess water evaporates leaving the cement and sand to gradually harden into a solid mass. The hardening of the mortar becomes noticeable some few hours after mixing and is complete in a few days. The usual mix of cement and sand for mortar is 1 part cement to 3 or 4 parts sand by volume, mixed with just sufficient water to render the mixture plastic.

A mortar of cement and sand is very durable and is used for all brickwork below ground level and all brickwork exposed to weather above roof level such as parapet walls and chimney stacks.

Cement mortar made with washed sand is not as plastic however as bricklayers would like it to be. Also when used with some types of bricks it can cause an unsightly effect known as efflorescence. This word describes the appearance of an irregular white coating on the face of bricks, caused by minute crystals of water-soluble salts in the brick. The salts go into solution in water inside the bricks and when the water evaporates in dry weather they are left on the face of bricks or plaster. Because cement mortar has greater compressive strength than required for most ordinary brickwork and because it is not very plastic, it is not recommended for general brickwork but instead a mixture of lime and cement with sand is used.

Lime: Lime is manufactured by burning limestone or chalk and the result of this burning is a dirty white lumpy material known as quicklime. When this quicklime is mixed with water a chemical change occurs during which heat is generated in the lime and water, and the lime expands to about three times its former bulk. This change is gradual and takes some days to complete, and the quicklime afterwards is said to be slaked, that is it has no more thirst for water. More precisely the lime is said to be hydrated, which means much the same thing. Obviously the quicklime must be slaked before it is used in mortar otherwise the mortar would increase in bulk and squeeze out of the joints. Lime for building is delivered to the site ready slaked and is termed 'hydrated lime'.

When mixed with water, lime combines chemically with carbon dioxide in the air and in undergoing this change it gradually hardens into a solid mass which firmly binds the sand.

A lime mortar is usually mixed with 1 part of lime to 3 parts sand by volume. The mortar is plastic and easy to spread and hardens into a dense mass of good compressive strength. A lime mortar readily absorbs water and in time the effect is to reduce the adhesion of the lime to the sand and the mortar crumbles and falls out of the joints in the brickwork.

Mortar for general brickwork is usually made from a mixture of cement, lime and sand in the proportions set out in table 6. These mixtures combine the strength of cement with the plasticity of lime, have much the same porosity as most bricks and do not cause efflorescence on the face of the brickwork.

Table 6 Mortar Mixes

	Mortar mix	
	Bricks	Concrete blocks
Internal walls and inner leaf of cavity walls	5	5
External walls		
above d.p.c.	4	4
below d.p.c.	3	3
Parapet walls, chimneys	2	3
Sills, copings, retaining walls	1	2

Mortar mix 5–1:3:10–12
cement, 4–1:2:8–9
lime, 3–1:1:5–6
sand, 2–1:$\frac{1}{2}$:4–4$\frac{1}{2}$
1–1:0–$\frac{1}{4}$:3

Mortar mix 5–1:8
cement, 4–1:7–8
sand, 3–1:5–6
plasticiser 2–1:3–4

Adapted from *BRE Digest 160*

Hydraulic lime is made by burning a mixture of chalk or limestone that contains clay. Hydraulic lime is stronger than ordinary lime and will harden in wet conditions,

hence the name. Ordinary Portland cement, made from similar materials and burned at a higher temperature, has largely replaced hydraulic lime which is little used today.

Mortar plasticisers

Liquids known as mortar plasticisers are manufactured. When these liquids are added to water they effervesce, that is the mixture becomes bubbly like soda water. If very small quantities are added to mortar, when it is mixed, the millions of minute bubbles that form surround the hard sharp particles of sand and so make the mortar plastic and easy to spread. The particular application of these mortar plasticisers is that if they are used with cement mortar they increase its plasticity and there is no need to use lime. It seems that the plasticisers do not adversely affect the hardness and durability of the mortar and they are commonly and successfully used for mortars.

Mortar mixes

A range of five mortar mixes is set out in table 6, and the application of these mixes to foundations, retaining walls, parapets and general walling is set out. These mortar mixes are recommended in *BRE Digest 160*.

Pointing

The word pointing is used to describe the filling of the mortar joints in the external faces of brickwork. Brickwork is pointed for two reasons: (a) to ensure that all horizontal and vertical mortar joints in external brickwork are solidly filled with mortar to make them watertight, and (b) for decorative reasons. The appearance of brickwork can be varied considerably by the use of coloured mortar for pointing and by making the pointing recessed or protruding.

Most brickwork joints today are filled as the brickwork is built and the operation is termed jointing. The bricklayers fill the external joints with mortar and finish them flush or recessed as they build the wall. This method of jointing is quite cheap. If, however, the joints are to be filled with some mortar of a different colour from that of the general mortar used for brickwork, or if the joints are to be shaped, then the operation is termed pointing and it is executed as an operation separate from bricklaying. As the brickwork is built the mortar joints to be pointed are raked out some 20 deep and the joints are filled or pointed later when the scaffold is being taken down.

The finished mortar joints may be either flush, recessed or projecting as shown in Fig. 61. The type of joint used is entirely a matter of taste.

Coloured pointing is executed with mortar pigmented with coloured cements, by the addition of lime or coloured sand or with stone dust, separately or in various combinations. Sometimes the horizontal joints are pointed with one colour of mortar and the vertical joints with mortar of a different colour. The coloured pointing may be finished with a flush, recessed or protruding joint. Pointing brickwork is a comparatively expensive operation.

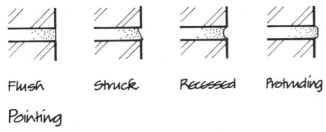

Flush   Struck   Recessed   Protruding

Pointing

Fig. 61

BUILDING BLOCKS

Building blocks are wall units larger in size than a brick that can be handled by one man. Building blocks are made of concrete or clay.

Concrete blocks

These are extensively used for both loadbearing and non-loadbearing walls, externally and internally. A concrete block wall can be laid in about half the time and it costs up to half as much as a similar brick wall. Lightweight aggregate concrete blocks have good insulating properties against transfer of heat and are much used for the inner skin of cavity walls either with a brick outer skin or a concrete block outer skin.

The disadvantage of concrete blocks as a wall unit is that they suffer moisture movement which may cause cracking of applied finishes such as plaster. To minimise cracking due to shrinkage by loss of water vertical movement joints should be built into long block walls at intervals of up to twice the height of the wall. These movement joints may be either a continuous vertical joint filled with mastic or they may be formed in the bonding of the blocks.

Because the block units are comparatively large any settlement movement in a wall will show more pronounced cracking in mortar joints than is the case with the smaller brick wall unit.

For use as a facing material a wide range of concrete blocks is manufactured from accurate fairface blocks to rugged exposed aggregate finishes.

Standard concrete blocks to British Standard 2028, 1364:1968 *Precast concrete blocks*, are manufactured as solid, hollow or cellular blocks from cement and either dense or lightweight aggregates. There are three types of block, Type A, dense concrete blocks, density not less than 1500 kg/m³ and Types B and C, lightweight concrete blocks, density less than 1500 kg/m³ but more than 625 kg/mm³. The three types are as follows:

Type A. Dense aggregate concrete blocks for general use in building including below ground: The standard dimensions of these blocks are 390 long × 90 or 190 high × 75, 90, 100, 140 or 190 thick; or 440 long × 215 high × 75, 90, 100, 140, 190 or 215 thick.

The blocks are made of Portland cement, natural aggregate or blast-furnace slag. The usual mix is 1 part of cement to 6 or 8 of aggregate by volume. These blocks are as heavy per cubic metre as bricks, they are not good

thermal insulators and their strength in resisting crushing is less than that of most well-burned bricks. The colour and texture of these blocks is far from attractive and they are usually either painted or covered with a coat of cement rendering. These blocks are used for internal and external loadbearing walls.

Type B. Lightweight aggregate concrete blocks for general use in building including below ground, in internal walls and inner leaf of cavity walls: The standard dimensions are 390 long × 90 or 190 high × 75, 90, 100, 140 and 190 thick; or 440 long × 190, 215 or 290 high × 75, 90, 100, 140, 190 and 215 thick; or 590 long × 190 or 215 high and 75, 90, 100, 140, 190 and 215 thick. The blocks are made of ordinary Portland cement and one of the following lightweight aggregates: granulated blast-furnace slag, foamed blast-furnace slag, expanded clay or shale, or well-burned furnace clinker. The usual mix is 1 part cement to 6 or 8 of aggregate by volume.

Of the four lightweight aggregates noted, well-burned furnace clinker produces the cheapest block which is about two-thirds the weight of a similar dense aggregate concrete block and is a considerably better thermal insulator. Blocks made from foamed blast-furnace slag are about twice the price of those made from furnace clinker but they are only half the weight of a similar dense aggregate block and have very good thermal insulating properties. The furnace clinker blocks are used extensively for walls of houses and the foamed blast-furnace slag blocks for walls of large framed buildings because of their lightness in weight.

Type C. Lightweight aggregate concrete blocks primarily for internal non-loadbearing walls: The standard dimensions are 390 long × 190 high × 60 or 75 thick; 440 long × 190, 215 and 290 high × 60 and 75 thick; 590 long × 190 and 215 high × 60 and 75 thick. The blocks are made with the same lightweight aggregate as those in Type B. These blocks are more expensive than dense aggregate blocks and are used principally for non-loadbearing partitions. These blocks are manufactured as solid, hollow or cellular depending largely on the thickness of the block, the thin blocks being solid, and the thicker either hollow or cellular to reduce weight and the drying shrinkage of the blocks. Figure 62 is an illustration of typical blocks.

Moisture movement: As water dries out from these precast concrete blocks the shrinkage that occurs may cause serious cracking of plaster and rendering applied to the surface of a wall built with them. Obviously the wetter the blocks the more they will shrink. It is essential that these blocks be protected on building sites from saturation by rain both when they are stacked on site before use and whilst walls are being built. Clay bricks are small and suffer very little drying shrinkage and therefore do not need to be protected from saturation by rain. Only the edges of these blocks should be wetted to increase their adhesion to mortar when the blocks are being laid.

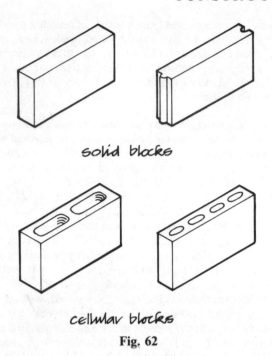

solid blocks

cellular blocks

Fig. 62

Bonding: Standard precast concrete blocks are laid in stretcher bond as there is no need to bond into the thickness of the wall, the various thickness of blocks are made to suit most wall thickness requirements. Quoin blocks, cavity blocks and half length and full length blocks are made. Loadbearing concrete blockwork is bonded at quoins or angles as illustrated in Fig. 63.

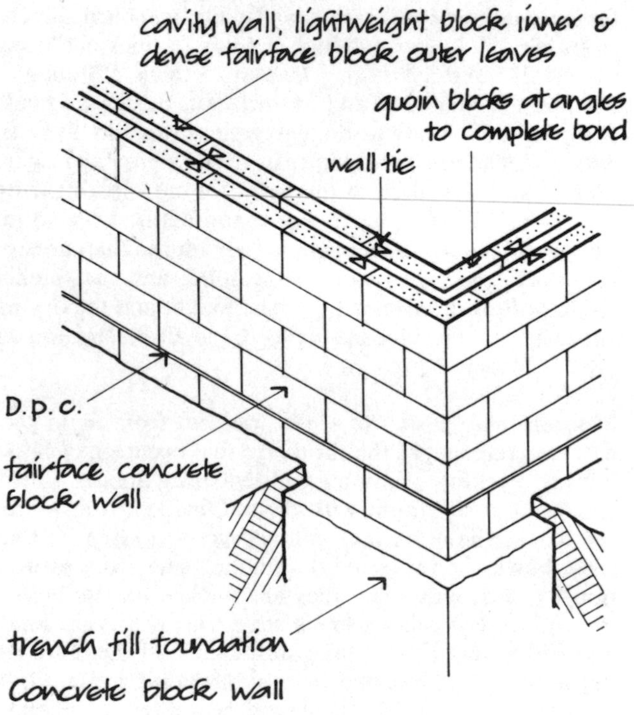

cavity wall, lightweight block inner & dense fairface block outer leaves

quoin blocks at angles to complete bond

wall tie

D.p.c.

fairface concrete block wall

trench fill foundation
Concrete block wall

Fig. 63

At junctions of loadbearing concrete block walls it is considered good practice to butt the end face of one wall to the other with a continuous vertical joint to accommodate shrinkage movements and minimise cracking of plaster finishes. Where one intersecting concrete block wall serves as a buttress to another, the butt joint should be reinforced by building in split end wall ties at each horizontal joint and across the vertical butt joint to bond the intersecting walls. Similarly, non-loadbearing concrete block walls should be butt jointed at intersections and the joint may be reinforced with strips of expanded metal in horizontal joints, Fig. 73.

Mortar: A cement mortar must not be used with concrete blocks. If a cement rich mortar, such as 1 part of cement to 3 parts sand is used the drying shrinkage of the mortar will be much greater than that of the blocks and serious cracking of plaster and rendering will almost certainly occur. A mortar with roughly the same density, strength and drying shrinkage as the blocks must be used and recommended mortar mixes are: 1 part cement to 1 part of lime to 6 of sand by volume or 1 part of cement to 2 parts of lime to 9 parts of sand by volume.

Clay blocks
Hollow clay building blocks to British Standard 3921: 1974 *Clay bricks and blocks*, are made for use as a wall unit. The blocks are made from selected brick clays that are press moulded and burnt. These hard, dense blocks are hollow to reduce shrinkage during firing and reduce their weight and they are grooved to provide a key for plaster as illustrated in Fig. 64. The standard block is 290 long × 215 high × 62.5, 75, 100 and 150 thick.

Clay blocks are comparatively lightweight, do not suffer moisture movement, have good resistance to damage by fire and poor thermal insulating properties. These blocks are mainly used for non-loadbearing partitions.

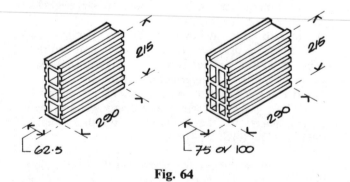

215

290

62.5

215

290

75 or 100

Fig. 64

The following is a description of some of the commonly accepted methods of constructing walls of brick and block to satisfy the functional requirements of stability, strength, exclusion of rain and thermal properties of buildings of up to three storeys.

Stability

For stability in supporting loads and against lateral forces, walls are built of bricks and blocks laid in mortar and bonded so that the building units act together as a wall.

For stability and strength the least thickness of a wall is determined in relation to its height and length. Where walls are laterally restrained, that is, stiffened against overturning by floors, the effective height of the wall is defined as the height of the wall either from its base on the foundation to the underside of the first floor, or roof tie, the underside of intermediate floors or upper floor to roof tie, or from the base of a gable, separating or compartment walls to the eaves, base of gable or half the height of gable as illustrated in Fig. 67.

Walls are laterally restrained by floors and roofs built into or anchored to them. For this lateral restraint to be effective against loss of stability by overturning, the floors must be solidly built into walls or firmly anchored to the wall. Figure 66 is an illustration of methods of building in concrete floors and of anchoring timber floors to walls by means of metal ties. It is because of this lateral restraint that the effective height of a wall is measured between floors.

Length is defined as the measurement from the centre of buttressing walls, piers or chimneys as illustrated in Fig. 65. Walls are stiffened or buttressed by end walls, separating walls, compartment walls, piers or chimneys which are bonded to them and contribute to the stability of the wall. Obviously at a junction the two walls act to buttress one another. Figure 65 is an illustration of buttresses to walls as defined in The Building Regulations. The minimum thickness of external, separating and compartment walls, set out in The Building Regulations

1976, is illustrated in Fig. 68, from which it will be seen that the higher the wall the thicker it should be at its base.

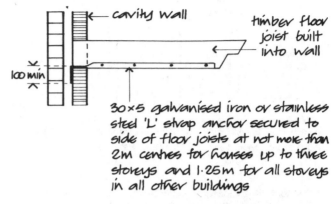

30×5 galvanised iron or stainless steel 'L' strap anchor secured to side of floor joists at not more than 2m centres for houses up to three storeys and 1·25m for all storeys in all other buildings

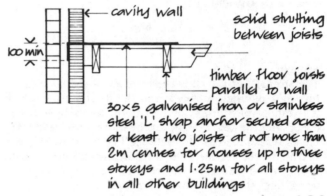

30×5 galvanised iron or stainless steel 'L' strap anchor secured across at least two joists at not more than 2m centres for houses up to three storeys and 1·25m for all storeys in all other buildings

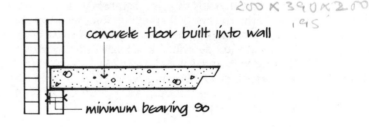

Floors providing lateral restraint to walls

Fig. 66

Length of walls

Fig. 65

Height of walls

Fig. 67

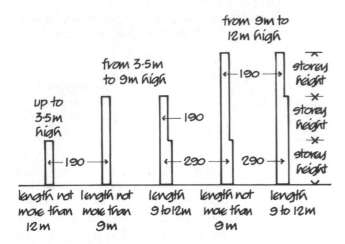

Minimum thickness of external, compartment and separating walls

Fig. 68

A solid 1*B* thick wall has adequate strength to support the load of floors and roofs of small buildings, such as houses. It would be wasteful, therefore, from the point of view of strength, to thicken the wall to exclude rain in positions of moderate and severe exposure. In addition the increase in thickness of a solid wall does not add appreciably to its thermal insulating properties.

For these reasons the, now common, external cavity wall was first used early this century, the wall being built as two skins or leaves of brickwork separated by a 50 cavity whose initial purpose was to act as a barrier to the penetration of rain to the inside face. Following the Second World War there was a shortage of bricks and concrete blocks came to be used as a substitute for bricks in the inner skin of cavity walls. At the same time demands for improved heating led to the use of light-weight concrete blocks for the inner skin of cavity walls to improve insulation and conserve heat.

Strength

The strength of a wall is the product of the strength of the units of brick or block and the mortar from which it is built. With bricks or blocks of the same strength, the greater the load the thicker the wall should be to carry the increased load as illustrated in Fig. 68. It will be seen that increased thickness at the base contributes to both strength and stability requirements. As an alternative to increasing thickness with increased load it is often economic, in walls of several storeys height, to maintain a uniform thickness throughout the height of the wall by using bricks of greater strength at the base of the wall. Such walls are described as designed or calculated load-bearing walls and walls whose thickness varies with height as prescribed loadbearing walls (that is prescribed by Regulations). The thickening of prescribed walls does not appreciably improve thermal insulation.

Exclusion of rain

The requirements of an external wall to exclude rain depend on the notional exposure of the wall to driving rain. The Building Research Station have developed an 'Index of exposure to driving rain' as sheltered, moderate and severe exposure and this index is explained in *BRS Digest 127*. The exposure depends on the position of a building in sheltered sites in towns or valleys, in moder-ately exposed sites in open country and severe exposure on high ground near the coast. Site visits and local information about the construction and resistance of existing buildings should be used to augment information from the index of exposure to driving rain.

A solid 1½*B* thick wall in sheltered positions is generally sufficiently thick to prevent rain penetrating to its inner face. In situations of moderate exposure, rain may well penetrate to the inner face and in exposed positions rain will almost certainly penetrate to the inner face of a 1½*B* thick solid wall.

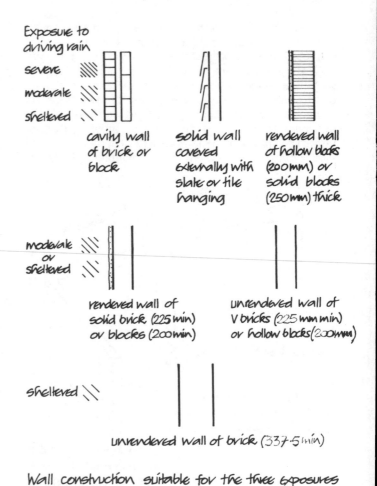

Wall construction suitable for the three exposures to driving rain

Fig. 69

Table 7

Exposure	Wall type	Construction			Minimum thickness (mm)
Severe	Cavity	Of brick or blockwork			—
	Single-leaf	Wall clad externally by tile-hanging, slate-hanging, etc.			—
		Rendered blockwork	Hollow blocks of dense or lightweight aggregate concrete with horizontal bed joint in two separate strips		200
			Solid aerated concrete blocks		250
Moderate	Single-leaf	Brickwork	Rendered		225
			Unrendered perforated through-the-wall brick (such as V-63) with horizontal bed joint in two separate strips		225
		Rendered blockwork	Fired-clay hollow blocks with horizontal bed joint in two separate strips		150
			Dense or lightweight aggregate concrete or solid aerated concrete blocks		200
		Unrendered blockwork	Specially designed fired-clay hollow blocks with horizontal bed joint in two separate strips		150
			Dense or lightweight aggregate hollow blocks with horizontal bed joint in two separate strips		200
Sheltered	Single-leaf	Brickwork	Unrendered		337.5
		Rendered blockwork	Solid or hollow block of fired clay or concrete		100

Adapted from Table 3, CP 121: Part 1: 1973

Some recommendations for wall construction in relation to exposure are set out in table 7. From the table it will be seen that a solid wall is suitable for sheltered exposure, a solid wall rendered for moderate exposure, and a solid wall protected with slate or tile hanging for severe exposure, whereas a cavity wall is suitable for all exposures. Figure 69 is an illustration of walls suitable for the three conditions of exposure.

Rendering is applied to a wall either for the sake of appearance or to improve resistance to rain penetration or both. Rendering (see Volume 2) is a wet mix of cement and sand or cement, lime and sand which when spread on the face of a wall and trowelled smooth or textured dries and hardens. The surface of a wall to be rendered has to be prepared by using keyed Flettons or the mortar joints have to be raked out to provide a key or bond to which the rendering can adhere.

Slate and tile hanging: In exposed positions walls are often protected with slate or tile hanging, the slates or tiles being nailed, or hung and nailed to wood battens fixed to the wall as illustrated in Fig. 70. Tile hanging is mostly used in the south and midland counties of England both on solid brick and block walls and as an external weathering to timber framed walls. Slate hanging is mostly used in northern and coastal areas of England and in Wales on brick, block and timber framed walls as a protection against driving rain.

Thermal properties
To maintain reasonable conditions of thermal comfort in buildings and to economise on fuel it is accepted that walls should provide a minimum resistance to the transfer of heat. The Building Regulations 1976 set maximum U values for walls of dwellings, that is, maximum thermal transmittance coefficient values. The maximum U values for walls of dwellings is 1.0 $W/m^2 °C$ and the maximum average value for perimeter walling (including any opening) is 1.8 $W/m^2 °C$. The First Amendment, 1978, Part FF sets lower maximum values for buildings other than dwellings. Solid walls and brick cavity walls do not by themselves provide a sufficiently low U value. It is therefore necessary to add some insulating material

to cavity walls, such as a lightweight block inner skin, cavity fill or an insulating lining. Figure 71 is an illustration of some of the deemed-to-satisfy wall sections to provide sufficient insulation to domestic buildings to comply with The Building Regulations.

It will be seen from Fig. 71 that solid walls have an insulating lining applied to the inside face and cavity walls have a cavity fill or an insulating lining fixed to the cavity side of the inside of the inner leaf or a lightweight block inner leaf.

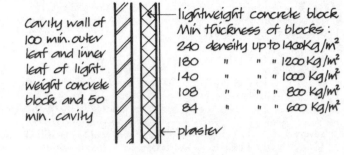

Cavity wall of 100 min. outer leaf and inner leaf of light-weight concrete block and 50 min. cavity

— lightweight concrete block
Min thickness of blocks:
240 density up to 1400 Kg/m²
180 " " " 1200 Kg/m²
140 " " " 1000 Kg/m²
108 " " " 800 Kg/m²
84 " " " 600 Kg/m²
← plaster

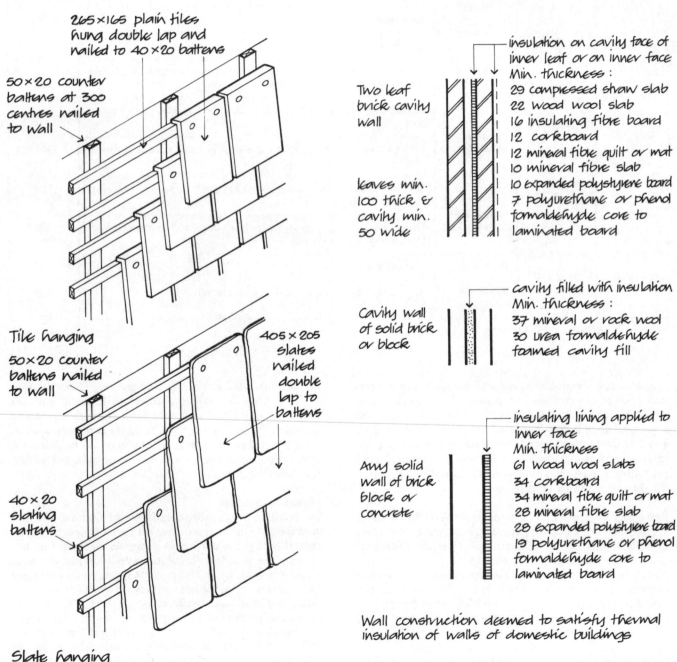

265×165 plain tiles hung double lap and nailed to 40×20 battens

50×20 counter battens at 300 centres nailed to wall

Tile hanging

50×20 counter battens nailed to wall

40×20 slating battens

405×205 slates nailed double lap to battens

Slate hanging

Two leaf brick cavity wall

leaves min. 100 thick & cavity min. 50 wide

insulation on cavity face of inner leaf or on inner face
Min. thickness:
29 compressed straw slab
22 wood wool slab
16 insulating fibre board
12 corkboard
12 mineral fibre quilt or mat
10 mineral fibre slab
10 expanded polystyrene board
7 polyurethane or phenol formaldehyde core to laminated board

Cavity wall of solid brick or block

cavity filled with insulation
Min. thickness:
37 mineral or rock wool
30 urea formaldehyde foamed cavity fill

Any solid wall of brick block or concrete

insulating lining applied to inner face
Min. thickness
61 wood wool slabs
34 corkboard
34 mineral fibre quilt or mat
28 mineral fibre slab
28 expanded polystyrene board
19 polyurethane or phenol formaldehyde core to laminated board

Wall construction deemed to satisfy thermal insulation of walls of domestic buildings

Fig. 70   **Fig. 71**

Thermal insulating materials: The materials used for thermal insulation with solid and cavity walls are manufactured as:

Lightweight concrete blocks
Rigid boards
Foamed plastic
Dry loose fill

Lightweight concrete blocks are very extensively used as the inner skin of cavity walls to provide insulation and adequate support for the floors and roof of small buildings. By themselves these blocks provide sufficient thermal insulation for domestic buildings to the standard of The Building Regulations. For other building uses either thicker blocks have to be used or some additional insulation must be incorporated.

Rigid boards are made from glass fibre, mineral fibre, polyurethene foam, expanded PVC or extruded polystyrene foam. The materials are supplied in lightweight, rigid board form in a variety of thicknesses from 12.5 mm to 150, lengths from 1200 to 3000 and widths from 75 to 1000. The boards may have a natural finish or be finished with vapour barriers or surfaces suitable for decorating, such as plasterboard.

These lightweight boards are used for thermal insulation inside the cavity against a dense block inner skin so that the solid inner skin can act as a thermal store or on the inside face of cavity and solid walls where they are fixed with adhesives, nailed to the block inner skin or to battens fixed to the wall as illustrated in Fig. 71. A high degree of thermal insulation can be obtained by the use of comparatively thin boards.

Cavity fill: Foamed plastic or dry loose fill may be used to fill the cavity of a cavity wall. This considerably improves the thermal insulation of the wall.

Urea formaldehyde resin, water and a foaming and hardening agent are mixed and poured or injected into the cavity. Here the material hardens into a rigid lightweight solid cavity filling. The wet material may be poured or injected into cavities as walls are built, or injected into the cavity of existing walls. This material will not normally act as a capillary path for water across the cavity.

A dry fill of polystyrene beads is used to fill the cavity of a cavity wall as it is built. This dry fill is poured into the cavity and will not normally provide a path for water to bridge the cavity by capillarity and serves as an efficient thermal insulator.

To be wholly effective an insulation used in a cavity of a cavity wall either in the form of boards, foamed fill or dry fill must extend the full width and height of the cavity up to the jambs, heads and sills of openings and down to ground floor level, and up to the level of roof insulation.

The resistance of a material to the transfer of heat is dependent on its density; the lower the density the higher the resistance. Table 8 sets out the density and resistance of common building materials.

Table 8

Material	Thickness (mm)	Density (kg/m²)	Resistance (m² °C/W)
Asbestos cement sheet	5	1600	0.013
Asphalt roofing	19	2250	0.016
Bitumen felt roofing	10	1100	0.05
Brickwork	105	1700	0.125
Concrete block			
lightweight	100	1200	0.30
dense	200	2100	0.18
Concrete	150	2100	0.12
Corkboard	13	130	0.32
Expanded polystyrene	13	15	0.37
Expanded polyurethane	13	30	0.57
Fibreboard	13	240	0.25
Glass sheet	3	2500	0.003
Mineral fibre	25	12	0.66
Plaster-gypsum	5	1300	0.01
Wood wool slabs	51	400	0.59

Cavity walls

If, instead of building a solid wall with the bricks or blocks bonded along the length and into the thickness of the wall, two separate skins are built with an air space or cavity between, the result will be a wall with better resistance to the penetration of rain. Walls built in this way with two skins or leaves separated by a 50 wide air space, or cavity, have been used for many years and are very satisfactory. The height to which such a wall can safely be built must be limited because in effect the wall is no more stable than each skin, as there is no bonding into the thickness of the wall. The vertical stability of the two separate skins can be, and always is, improved by building metal ties across the cavity in such a way that the ends of the ties are bedded in the horizontal mortar joints of each skin. By virtue of the wall ties the cavity wall is nearly as stable as a solid wall of the same thickness as the two skins.

Solid filling of cavity at foundation: It has been usual to show a fine concrete filling of the base of the cavity of the cavity wall at foundation level, the purpose of which is to strengthen the wall. If the wall requires additional strength it would be wise to build a solid $1\frac{1}{2}B$ wall at the base with a cavity wall above. The likelihood is that the solid filling represents the almost inevitable accumulation of mortar droppings rather than a purposive addition to the wall.

Cavity wall ties: There are three patterns of metal ties in common use – the galvanised iron twisted tie, the double triangle tie and the galvanised wire butterfly tie. The twisted iron tie has fish-tailed ends to give good bond to mortar and is twisted in its middle so that water cannot run across it to the inner skin of the cavity wall, as shown in Fig. 72. The butterfly pattern should be laid with the ends of the wire and the double triangle type with the bend hanging down into the cavity so that water will drip off.

It is thought by some that the butterfly type is not a good design as mortar may fall into the cavity whilst the brickwork is being built and lodge in the triangle of the tie. If there is a fair sized blob of mortar right across the tie the mortar will probably get saturated by contact with the outer skin of the brickwork and in turn make the inner skin of the wall wet.

The usual intervals at which ties are built into cavity walls are 900 horizontally and 450 vertically as illustrated in Fig. 73, which is a view of part of a cavity wall and its foundation. It is usual to build the two separate skins of block or brickwork in ordinary stretcher bond.

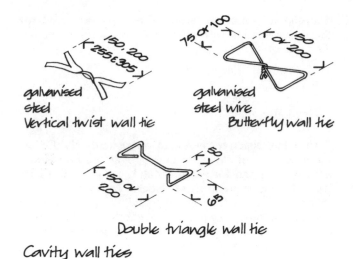

galvanised steel Vertical twist wall tie

galvanised steel wire Butterfly wall tie

Double triangle wall tie

Cavity wall ties

Fig. 72

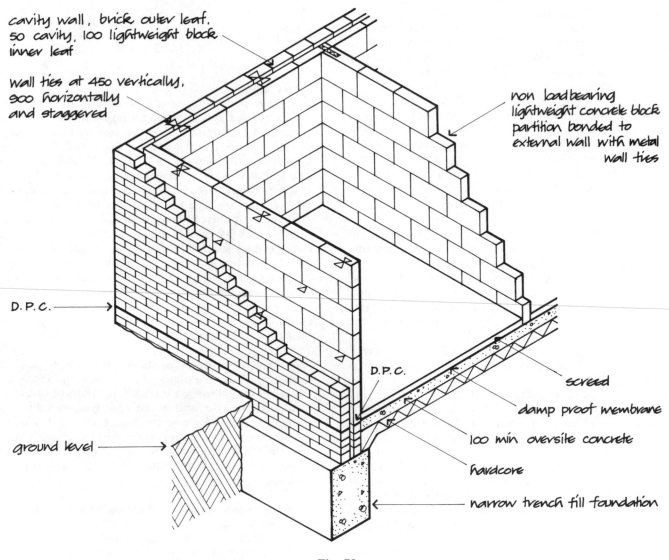

cavity wall, brick outer leaf, 50 cavity, 100 lightweight block inner leaf

wall ties at 450 vertically, 900 horizontally and staggered

non load bearing lightweight concrete block partition bonded to external wall with metal wall ties

D.P.C.

D.P.C.

screed

damp proof membrane

100 min oversite concrete

hardcore

ground level

narrow trench fill foundation

Fig. 73

The purpose of the cavity in this type of wall is to prevent rain penetrating to the inner skin and to improve the insulation of the wall. It is important, therefore, that the cavity be clear and unobstructed by solid material throughout its height and length. Nothing solid must bridge the cavity between the two skins of the wall other than the ties and lightweight insulating fill or lining. Any brick or mortar lodged in the cavity may allow water to pass through it to the inner skin and so defeat the object of the cavity. The bricklayers building a cavity wall must take precautions to prevent mortar or bits of brick from falling into the cavity. This is usually done by suspending a batten of wood, bound with sacking, in the cavity as the wall is built. This batten is raised, as the brickwork is built, and is withdrawn and cleaned from time to time.

Most solid brick or block cavity walls are built with a brick outer skin and a lightweight concrete block inner skin thus combining the durability, strength and appearance of brick with the insulating properties of lightweight blocks that have adequate strength to support the floors and roofs of houses.

OPENINGS IN BRICK AND BLOCK WALLS

Figure 74 is a view of a window opening in a brick wall and the terms used to describe the parts are noted.

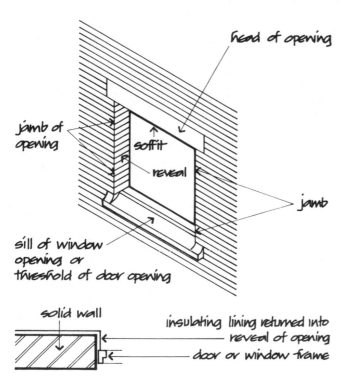

Fig. 74

Jambs

The term jamb derives from the French word *jambe* meaning leg. From Fig. 74, it will be seen that the brickwork on either side of the opening acts like legs which support brickwork over the head of the opening. The term jamb is not used to describe a particular width either side of openings and is merely a general term for the brickwork for full height of opening either side of the window. The word 'reveal' is used more definitely to describe the thickness of the wall revealed by cutting the opening and the reveal is a surface of brickwork as long as the height of the opening. The lower part of the opening is a sill for windows and a threshold for doors.

Plain or square jambs of openings: The majority of openings for windows and doors in solid and cavity brick and block walls are finished with plain or square jambs. The insulating lining fixed to the inner face of a solid wall of bricks or blocks is continued round the inner reveal of the opening as illustrated in Fig. 74. Most external walls are constructed as a cavity wall with the inner skin of lightweight concrete blocks, Type B, to provide thermal insulation.

Jambs of openings in cavity walls: It will be remembered that the cavity serves to prevent penetration of moisture from the outer to the inner skin. The cavity must, therefore, be closed at jambs to prevent cold air blowing into it and so reducing the insulating properties of the wall and any material which is used to close the cavity must be sufficiently non-absorbent to prevent moisture crossing it from the outer to the inner skins.

There are two ways of closing the cavity at jambs of openings: (a) by solidly closing the cavity with brick or block and building in a continuous vertical damp-proof course, or (b) by building in the timber or metal door or window frame so that it closes the cavity.

Solid closing of cavity: The cavity is closed either with brick or block and a continuous strip of bitumen-impregnated felt, lead-cored felt, or a strip of lead or copper is sandwiched in the cavity at the jambs of openings. This construction is illustrated in Fig. 75. It will be seen that the cavity is closed with blocks purposely made to close the cavity and that moisture is prevented from penetrating from the outer to the inner skin by a strip of vertical d.p.c. The strip of vertical d.p.c. material is tacked to the back of the wood frame. The purpose of this is to keep the d.p.c. in position while the wall is being built, and to protect the back of the frame from damp which may penetrate the outer skin of the wall. A strip of lead or copper can more easily be tacked to the back of the frame and then be bent for building in as vertical d.p.c. than can a strip of bituminous felt, and is sometimes preferred for this reason although more expensive than felt.

Obviously the strip of vertical d.p.c. must be at least as wide as the solid filling of the cavity and strips 150 wide are generally used.

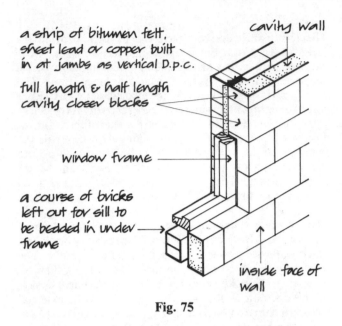

a strip of bitumen felt, sheet lead or copper built in at jambs as vertical D.p.c.

full length & half length cavity closer blocks

cavity wall

window frame

a course of bricks left out for sill to be bedded in under frame

inside face of wall

Fig. 75

Where a cavity fill or lining is used to provide insulation to a cavity wall of brick or block skins it is important that the cavity fill or lining be continued up to the back of the window or door frame so that the insulation is continuous along the wall between openings, as illustrated in Fig. 76. If the cavity at jambs of openings were to be solidly closed with brick or block the comparatively poor insulation of the brick or block would act as a cold bridge across the cavity.

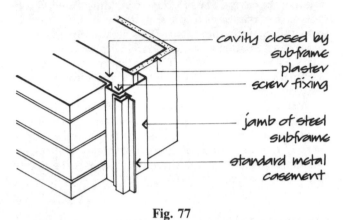

cavity closed by subframe
plaster
screw fixing

jamb of steel subframe

standard metal casement

Fig. 77

Closing cavity at jambs with frames: Most timber window and door frames are wider than 50 and can be used to close the cavity at jambs as shown in Fig. 76. Providing the external face of the timber frame is solidly bedded in mortar against the rebate behind the outer skin as shown in Fig. 76, the frame will successfully close the cavity and will prevent penetration of moisture from the outer to the inner skin of the cavity wall. Standard metal window frames are not as wide as a 50 cavity and cannot by themselves be used to close the cavity at jambs of window openings. Steel subframes for metal windows are designed to fit into and close the cavity as illustrated in Fig. 77. When standard metal windows are built into openings in cavity walls the cavity should be closed with a vertical d.p.c. as previously described and the window frame so positioned that the plaster on the inner reveal of the opening lies entirely behind the vertical d.p.c.

Rebated jambs: Window and door frames made of soft wood have to be painted for protection from rain, for if wood becomes saturated it swells and in time may decay. With some styles of architecture it is thought best to hide as much of the window frame as possible. So either as a partial protection against rain or appearances sake, or for both reasons, the jambs of openings are rebated.

Figure 78 shows a view of one rebated jamb on which the terms used are noted.

As one of the purposes of a rebated jamb is to protect the frame from rain the rebate faces into the building and the frame of the window or door is fixed behind the rebate.

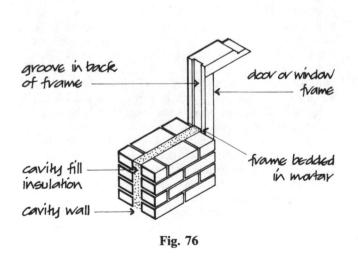

groove in back of frame

door or window frame

cavity fill insulation

cavity wall

frame bedded in mortar

Fig. 76

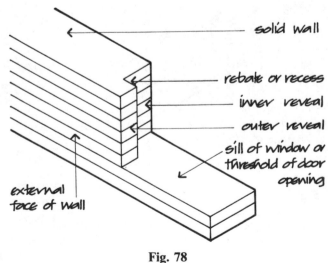

solid wall

rebate or recess
inner reveal
outer reveal
sill of window or threshold of door opening

external face of wall

Fig. 78

Outer reveal: The brickwork thickness revealed at the sides of the opening on the outside of the rebate is usually $\frac{1}{2}B$ wide for convenience in bonding the bricks. This outer reveal could of course be any width which is a multiple of $\frac{1}{2}B$, providing the wall is thick enough, but usually it is $\frac{1}{2}B$ wide and the width of the *inner* reveal must therefore be the difference between the width of the outer reveal and the thickness of the wall.

Rebate: The depth of the rebate or recess is usually $\frac{1}{4}B$ but for the cased frames of windows may be $\frac{1}{2}B$ deep. The depth of rebate is made a half of, or the width of, a brick for convience in bonding the bricks.

Bonding of bricks at jambs: Just as at an angle or quoin in brickwork, bricks specially cut have to be used to complete, or close, the $\frac{1}{4}B$ overlap caused by bonding, so at jambs special closer bricks $\frac{1}{4}B$ wide on face have to be used.

Provided that the outer reveal is $\frac{1}{2}B$ wide, the following basic rules will apply irrespective of the sort of bond used or the thickness of the wall. If the rebate is $\frac{1}{4}B$ deep the bonding at one jamb will be arranged as illustrated in Fig. 80. In every other course of bricks a header face and then a closer or $\frac{1}{4}B$ wide face must appear at the jamb or angle of opening. To do this and at the same time to form the $\frac{1}{4}B$ deep rebate and to avoid vertical joints continuously up the wall two cut bricks have to be used. These are a bevelled bat (note: a 'bat' is any cut part of a brick) which is shaped as shown in Fig. 80 and a king closer which is illustrated in Fig. 80 Neither of these bricks is made specially to the shape and size shown, but they are cut from whole bricks on the site.

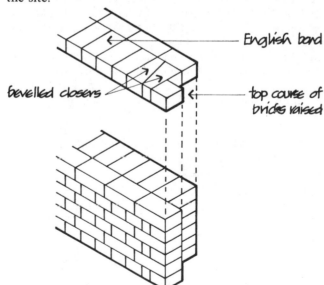

View of part of brickwork in rebated jamb showing bonding

Fig. 79

In the course above and below, two other cut bricks, called bevelled closers, should be used behind the stretcher brick. These two bricks are used so as to avoid a vertical joint. Figure 80 shows a view of a bevelled closer.

If the rebate is $\frac{1}{2}B$ deep and the outer reveal is $\frac{1}{2}B$ the bonding at jambs is shown in Fig. 79.

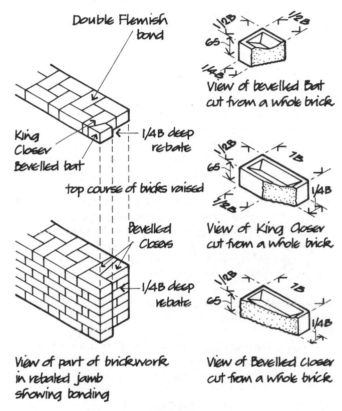

Fig. 80

Head of openings

The brickwork over the head of openings has to be supported either by a flat lintel or an arch. The brickwork which the lintel or arch has to support is a triangle with 60 degree angles, as in Fig. 81.

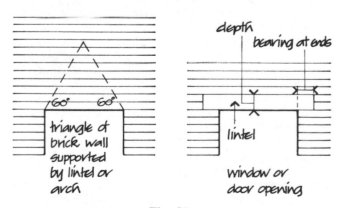

Fig. 81

The triangle is formed by the vertical joints between bricks which overlap $\frac{1}{4}B$. In a bonded wall if the brickwork inside the triangle were taken out the rest of the wall above would be quite safe. This is another reason for bonding bricks.

Lintels: This is the name given to any single solid length of concrete, steel, timber or stone built in over an opening to support the wall over it, as shown in Fig. 81. The ends of the lintel must be built into the brick or blockwork over the jambs so as to convey the weight carried by the lintel to the jambs. The area of wall on which the end of a lintel bears is termed its *bearing* at ends. The wider the opening the more weight the lintel has to support and the greater its bearing at ends must be so as to transmit the load it carries to an area capable of supporting it. For convenience in building the ends of a lintel into brickwork its depth is usually made a multiple of brick course height, that is 75, and the lintels are not usually less than 150 deep.

Timber lintels: Up to about sixty years ago it was common practice to support the brickwork over openings on a timber lintel. Wood lintels are not used today because the wood may be damaged during a fire and so cause the collapse of the wall above it and also because timber is liable to rot, again causing the wall over it to collapse.

Stone lintels: These are explained in the chapter on masonry in Volume 2.

Concrete lintels: Most lintels used today are of concrete, which is usually reinforced with steel rods. Concrete is a reasonably cheap material, it can easily be moulded or cast when wet and when it hardens it has very good strength in resisting crushing and does not lose strength or otherwise deteriorate when exposed to the weather. The one desirable quality that concrete lacks, if it is to be used as a lintel, is tensile strength, that is strength to resist being pulled apart. The following is an explanation of the behaviour of a lintel when supporting brickwork and the reason for and position of reinforcement in concrete.

Suppose that the lintel over an opening were made of india rubber. When the bricks over the opening are laid the india rubber lintel would bend as shown in Fig. 82. Now if we bend a piece of india rubber as the lintel here is bent and look at it closely we will see that the top surface is squeezed together and the bottom surface is considerably stretched. A squeezing together indicates compression and a stretching, tension. A concrete lintel will not bend so obviously as does india rubber under the weight of the brickwork over it, but it will bend very slightly and its top surface will be compressed and its bottom surface stretched or in tension. Concrete is strong in resisting compression but weak in resisting tension, and to give the concrete lintel the strength required to resist the tension at its lower surface, steel is added to it because steel is strong in resisting tension. This is the

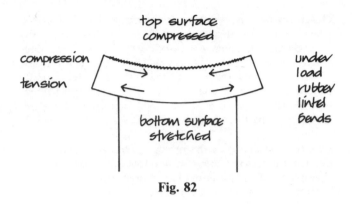

Fig. 82

reason why rods of steel are cast into the bottom of the lintel when it is being moulded in its wet state.

In fact the india rubber lintel used for the explanation above is not only squeezed up at its top surface and stretched at its bottom surface as can be seen if an india rubber is doubled over. If we examine a folded india rubber we see that it is compressed less and less looking down from the top of it and less and less stretched looking up from the bottom of it towards the centre of the rubber where it is neither stretched nor compressed. In exactly the same way a concrete lintel when carrying brickwork is stretched and compressed most at bottom and top surfaces and less so towards the centre of its depth. Lengths of steel rod are cast into concrete lintels to give them strength in resisting tensile or stretching forces. As the tension is greatest at the underside of the lintel it would seem sensible to cast the steel rods in the lowest surface. In fact the steel rods are cast in some 15 or more above the bottom surface. The reason for this is that steel very soon rusts when exposed to air and if the steel rods were in the lower surface of the lintel they would rust and in time give way and the lintel would collapse. Also if a fire occurs in the building the steel rods would, if cast in the surface, expand and come away from the concrete and the lintel would collapse. The rods are cast at least 15 up from the bottom of the lintel and the 15 or more of concrete below them is called the concrete cover.

Re-inforcing rods: These are usually of round section mild steel of 10 or 12 diameter for lintels up to 1.8 span. The ends of the rods should be bent up at 90° or hooked as in Fig. 83.

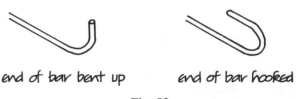

end of bar bent up   end of bar hooked

Fig. 83

The purpose of bending up the ends is to ensure that when the lintel does bend the rods do not lose their adhesion to the concrete around them. After being bent or hooked at the ends the rods should be some 50 or 75 less long than the lintel at either end. An empirical rule for determining the number of 12 rods required for lintels of up to say 1.8 span is to allow one 12 rod for each half brick thickness of wall which the lintel supports.

Casting lintels: The word 'precast' indicates that a concrete lintel has been cast inside a mould, and has been hardened before it is built into the wall.

The words 'situ-cast' indicate that the lintel is cast in position inside a timber mould fixed over the opening in walls. Whether the lintel is precast or situ-cast will not affect the finished result and which method is used will depend on which is most convenient. It is common practice to precast lintels for most normal door and window openings, the advantage being that immediately the lintel is placed in position the opening, brickwork can be raised on it whereas the concrete in a situ-cast lintel requires a timber mould or formwork and must be allowed to harden before brickwork can be raised on it.

Lintels are cast in-situ, that is in position over openings, if a precast lintel would have been too heavy or cumbersome to have been easily hoisted and bedded in position. Precast lintels must be clearly marked to make certain that they are bedded with the steel reinforcement in its correct place, at the bottom of the lintel. Usually the letter 'T' or the word 'Top' is cut into the top of the concrete lintel whilst it is still wet.

Prestressed concrete lintels: Prestressed precast concrete lintels are widely used particularly over internal openings. A prestressed lintel is made by casting concrete around high tensile stretched wires which are anchored to the concrete so that the concrete is compressed by the stress in the wires. (See also Volume 4.) Under load the compression of concrete, due to the stressed wires, has to be overcome before the lintel will bend.

Two types of prestressed concrete lintel are made, composite lintels and non-composite lintels.

Composite lintels, which are stressed by a wire or wires at the centre of their depth, are designed to be used with the brickwork they support which acts as a composite part of the lintel in supporting loads. These comparatively thin precast lintels are built in over openings and brickwork is built over them. Prestressed lintels over openings more than 1200 wide should be supported to avoid deflection, until the mortar in the brickwork has set. When used to support blockwork the composite strength of these lintels is considerably less than when used with brickwork.

Non-composite prestressed lintels are made for use where there is insufficient brickwork over to act compositely with the lintel and also where there are heavy loads.

These lintels are made to suit brick and block wall thicknesses as illustrated in Fig. 84. They are mostly used for internal openings, the inner skin of cavity walls and the outer skin where it is covered externally.

Concrete lintels in solid walls: A reinforced concrete or a prestressed lintel may be used over openings in external solid walls with the lintel exposed on the face of the wall or covered by rendering applied to the external face of the wall. Either one or two lintels may be used depending on the convenience of lifting and placing the lintels. The lintel is built into the jambs of the opening sufficient to spread the load. An insulating lining, fixed to the inside face of solid walls, is returned in the soffit of the opening.

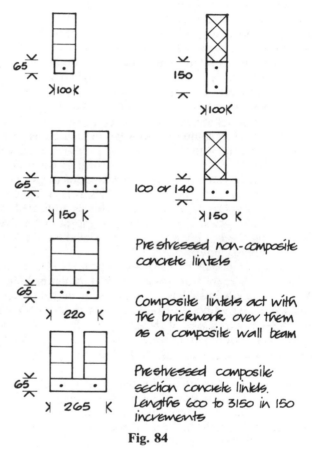

Prestressed non-composite concrete lintels

Composite lintels act with the brickwork over them as a composite wall beam

Prestressed composite section concrete lintels. Lengths 600 to 3150 in 150 increments

Fig. 84

Boot lintels: When concrete has dried it is dull light grey colour. Some think that a concrete lintel exposed for its full depth on the external face of brick walls is not attractive. In the past it was common practice to hide the concrete lintel behind a brick arch or brick lintel built over the opening externally. A modification of the ordinary rectangular section lintel, known as a boot lintel, is used to reduce the depth of the lintel exposed externally. Figure 85 shows a section through the head of an opening showing a boot lintel in position. The lintel is boot-shaped in section with the toe part showing externally. The toe is usually made 65 deep and this small depth of concrete showing over the opening does not spoil the appearance of the brickwork. The main body of the lintel is inside the wall where it does not show and it is this part of the lintel which does most of the work of supporting brickwork. Some think that the face of the brickwork looks best if the toe of the lintel finishes just 25 or 40 back from the external face of the wall, as in Fig. 86. The brickwork built on the toe of the lintel is usually $\frac{1}{2}B$ thick for openings up to 1.8 wide. The 65 deep toe, if reinforced as shown, is capable of safely carrying the two or three courses of $\frac{1}{2}B$ thick brickwork over it. The brickwork above the top of the main part of the lintel bears mainly on it because the bricks are bonded. If the opening is wider than 1.8 the main part of the lintel is sometimes made sufficiently thick to support most of the thickness of the wall over, as in Fig. 86. The brickwork resting on the toe of the lintel is built with bricks cut in half. When the toe of the lintel projects beyond the face of the brickwork it should be weathered to throw rainwater out from wall face and throated to prevent water running in along soffit or underside as shown in Fig. 85. When the external face of brickwork is in direct contact with concrete, as is the brickwork on the toe of this lintel, an efflorescence of salts is liable to appear on the face of the brickwork. This is caused by soluble salts in the concrete being withdrawn when the wall dries out after rain and being left on the face of the brickwork in the form of white dust. This looks ugly. To prevent it, the faces of the lintel in direct contact with the external brickwork should be painted with bituminous paint. This is indicated in Fig. 85. The bearing at ends where the boot lintel is bedded on the brick jambs should be of the same area as for ordinary lintels.

A boot lintel can be used over openings in a cavity wall only where the wall has an internal insulating lining. Where a cavity wall has an inner skin of lightweight blocks, a cavity fill or a cavity lining a boot lintel used to support both leaves of the cavity would act as a cold bridge through the lintel which has very poor insulating properties as compared to the wall above.

Lintels in cavity walls: Where the thermal insulation in a cavity wall is a cavity fill or a cavity lining applied to the inner skin, it is important that the fill and the lining be carried down to the head of the opening so that the whole of the wall is insulated.

Were the lintel to be built right across the cavity it would act as a cold bridge due to its poor insulating properties and would invite condensation on its inner face. It is, therefore, usual to use two separate lintels one for each of the two skins with the insulation run between them as illustrated in Fig. 87.

Where a lightweight concrete block inner skin is used as the insulation for a cavity wall it is important that either the insulating properties of the blocks be continued down to the head of the opening or that some insulating material be fixed between separate lintels supporting the inner and outer skins. There are on the market galvanised steel lintels specifically designed to support both the outer skin of a cavity wall and a course of lightweight concrete

blocks over the head of openings as illustrated in Fig. 88. It will be seen that the lintel is shaped to act as a cavity tray to collect any moisture in the cavity and direct it to the outside face of the wall. These lintels are made of mild steel which is cut, shaped and welded and then is hot dip galvanised (see also Volume 2) so that the whole of the lintel is coated with zinc against corrosion. The galvanised steel lintel, illustrated in Fig. 89, is designed for use over openings in internal walls.

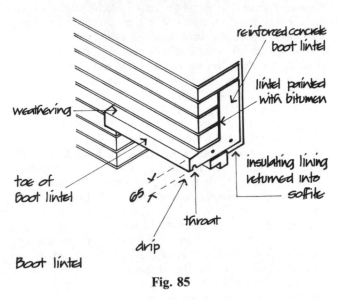

Boot lintel

Fig. 85

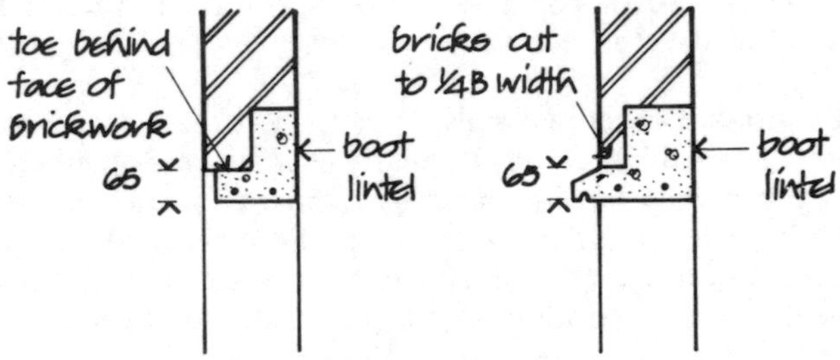

Fig. 86

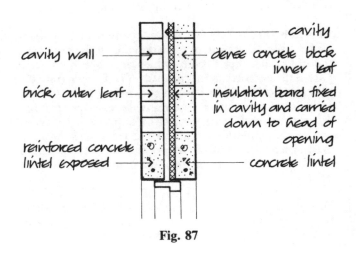

Fig. 87

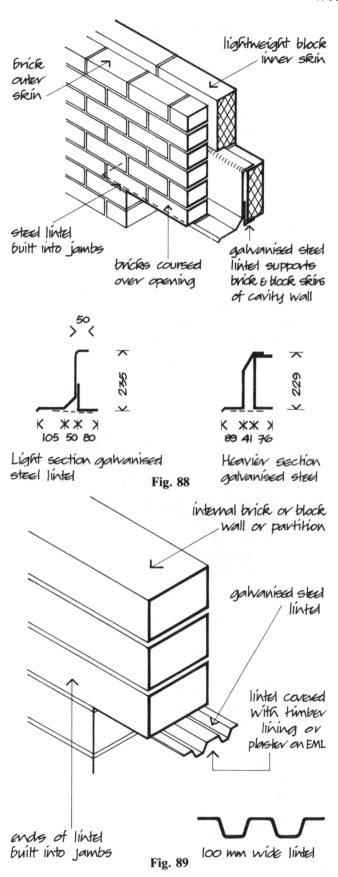

brick outer skin

lightweight block inner skin

steel lintel built into jambs

bricks coursed over opening

galvanised steel lintel supports brick & block skins of cavity wall

Light section galvanised steel lintel

Fig. 88

Heavier section galvanised steel

internal brick or block wall or partition

galvanised steel lintel

lintel covered with timber lining or plaster on EML

ends of lintel built into jambs

100 mm wide lintel

Fig. 89

D.p.c. and trays at head of openings in cavity walls: It has been common for some years to indicate the use of a d.p.c. or a cavity tray at the head of openings in cavity walls, the purpose of which was to collect moisture. The outer leaf of a cavity wall should be sufficiently thick or be protected by rendering or slate or tile hanging to prevent rain penetrating to the cavity. If the outer leaf of the cavity wall is an effective barrier to rain there seems little purpose in using a d.p.c. or cavity tray and the effective use of insulating cavity fills and insulating linings confirms this.

Brick lintels: A brick lintel may be formed as bricks on end, bricks on edge or coursed bricks laid horizontally over openings. The small units of brick, laid in mortar, give poor support to the wall above and usually need some form of additional support. A brick on-end lintel is generally known as a 'soldier arch' or 'brick on-end' arch. The word arch here is wrongly used as the bricks are not arranged in the form of an arch or curve but laid flat. The brick lintel is built with bricks laid on end with stretcher faces showing as in Fig. 90.

Bricks laid on edge, showing a header face, may be used as a lintel as illustrated in Fig. 90. It will be seen that there has to be a course of split bricks over the lintel. These bricks, cut down to a depth of 37 look untidy. Alternatively the soffit of the lintel can be laid out of line with brick courses (Fig. 90). Only the adhesion between mortar and the bricks keeps these lintels in place and in turn supports the brickwork over the lintel. If the opening over which the brick lintel is formed is wider than say 600 or 900 it is very likely that the adhesion between mortar and bricks in the lintel will weaken in time and one or more of the bricks will sink or even fall out of place. This will obviously look ugly and moreover the bricks above the lintel, which then have no adequate support, may sink. There are various methods of strengthening and giving support to brick lintels. Those following are some of them.

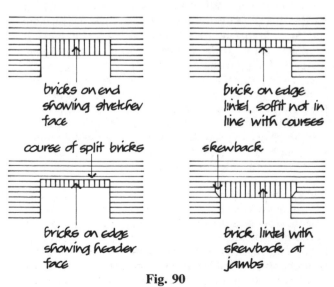

bricks on end showing stretcher face

brick on edge lintel, soffit not in line with courses

course of split bricks

skewback

bricks on edge showing header face

brick lintel with skewback at jambs

Fig. 90

49

For openings up to 900 wide it is generally satisfactory to cut the brick at either end of the lintel on the splay so as to form what is called a skew back, as shown in Fig. 90. It will be seen that the skew or slanting surface bears on a skew brick in the jamb and this improves the stability of the lintel. In building a brick lintel, mortar should be packed tightly between the bricks.

For openings more than 900 wide a brick lintel can be supported by a wrought iron bearing bar, the ends of which are built into brickwork jambs and on which the brick lintel bears (Fig. 91). The bar has bent, or cranked, ends for building into the vertical joints in brickwork at the jambs of the opening. This is not a satisfactory method of supporting the lintel as the bar is visible on the soffit of the lintel and looks ugly, and in time it will rust and look more ugly than it did when first built. Also the bar has a tendency to sag and the lintel may sag with it. As an alternative a mild steel angle section is built with its ends in the brickwork either side of the opening and supporting the lintel. The size of the angle usually used is 50×75. This is a satisfactory method of supporting the lintel but unless the door or window frame is fixed near the outside face of the wall the angle will show and in time will rust and look very unsightly.

Another method of support is to drill a hole in each brick of the lintel. This can only successfully be done with fine grained bricks such as Marls or Gaults. Through the holes in the bricks a round-section mild steel rod is threaded and the ends of the rod are built into the brickwork either side of the lintel. This method of supporting the lintel is quite satisfactory but is somewhat expensive because of the labour involved in drilling the bricks.

A brick lintel can be given support by wall ties bedded between bricks and cast into an in-situ cast lintel behind. The lintel is usually built on a timber board called a soffit board which is fixed between the jambs of the opening and is supported from below. As the bricklayer builds the brick lintel he beds a wall tie between the bricks as shown in Fig. 91. When the mortar between bricks has hardened a reinforced concrete lintel is cast in-situ behind the brick lintel so that when the concrete lintel has hardened the wall ties are cast into it. This is a sound method of supporting a brick lintel.

In recent years a galvanised steel support for brick lintels has been used. The steel lintel support is shaped for building in over openings and acts as a support for the brick lintel and as a cavity d.p.c. as illustrated in Fig. 88. A galvanised steel lintel is the most commonly used method of supporting brick lintels with the bricks either on end, on edge or coursed across the opening.

Brick arches: Figure 92 shows a semi-circular brick arch on which are noted the various terms used in arch work.

'Intrados' and 'extrados' are the names given to the inside and outside *lines* of curve of an arch. Soffit is the inside curved surface under the arch. The middle third of the arch is called the crown and the two lower thirds the haunches. Where the plain brickwork meets the

extrados of the arch there is an *abutment* of horizontal brickwork with the arch. The horizontal mortar joint or line from which the arch springs is called the springing line. Voussoir is the word used to describe each brick (or stone) used to form an arch.

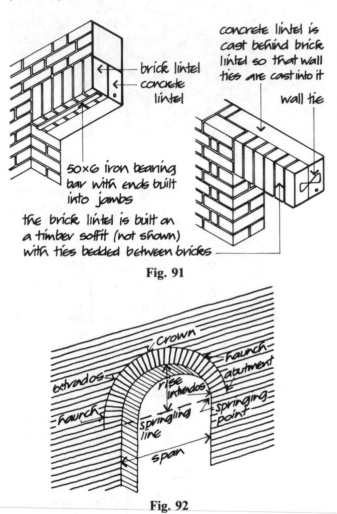

Fig. 91

Fig. 92

Rough, axed and gauged bricks: If bricks are used to form a curved arch either the mortar joints between the bricks must be wedge shaped or the bricks must be cut to a wedge shape and the joints be of uniform thickness, as shown in Fig. 93.

When an arch is built with wedge-shaped joints between bricks which have not been cut, the arch is said to be rough because the wedge-shaped joints look ugly and the finished effect of the arch is rough. Also in time the mortar joints, which may be quite thick at the top of the wedge, will tend to crack and the mortar crumble from the joints. Rough arches are not usually used for facing brickwork.

Axed bricks: Any good facing brick, no matter how hard, can be cut to a wedge shape on the building site. A template, or pattern, is cut from a sheet of zinc to the exact wedge shape to which the bricks are to be cut. The template is laid on the stretcher or header face of the brick as in Fig. 94. Shallow cuts are made in the face of the brick either side of the template. These cuts are made with a hacksaw blade or file, and are to guide the bricklayer in cutting the brick. Then, holding the brick in one hand the bricklayer gradually chops the brick to the required wedge shape. For this he uses a tool called a scutch illustrated in Fig. 94. When the brick has been cut to a wedge shape the rough, cut surfaces are made smooth with a coarse rasp which is a steel file with coarse teeth.

From the description this appears to be a laborious operation but in fact the skilled bricklayer can axe a brick to a wedge shape in a few minutes. The axed wedged shaped bricks are built to form the arch with uniform 10 thick mortar joints between the bricks.

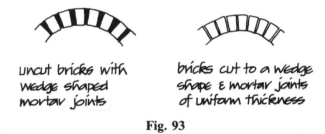

uncut bricks with wedge shaped mortar joints

bricks cut to a wedge shape & mortar joints of uniform thickness

Fig. 93

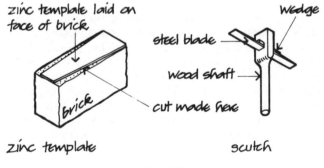

zinc template laid on face of brick

wedge

steel blade

wood shaft

cut made here

brick

zinc template

scutch

Fig. 94

Gauged bricks: The word gauge means measure, and gauged bricks are those that have been so accurately prepared to a wedge shape that they can be put together to form an arch with very thin joints between them. This does not improve the strength of the brick arch and is done entirely for reasons of appearance. Hard burned clay facing bricks cannot be cut to the accurate wedge shape required for this work because the bricks are too coarse grained, and bricks which are to be gauged are specially prepared. The type of brick used for gauged brickwork is called a rubber brick because its composition is such that it can be rubbed down to an accurate shape on a flat stone.

Rubber bricks are manufactured from fine grained sand and a small proportion of alumina or clay. The bricks are moulded and then baked to harden them, and the temperature at which these bricks are baked is lower than that at which clay bricks are burned, the aim being to avoid fusion of the material of the bricks so that they can easily be cut and accurately rubbed to shape. Rubber bricks have a fine sandy texture and are usually 'brick red' in colour although grey, buff and white rubber bricks are made. These bricks are usually larger than most clay bricks.

Gauged bricks for arch work: The arch to be built is drawn out full size and from this drawing, sheet zinc templates, or patterns, are cut to the exact size of the wedge-shaped brick voussoirs. These templates are placed on the stretcher face or header face of the rubber brick to be cut and the brick is sawn to a wedge shape with a brick saw which consists of an 'H'-shaped wooden frame across which is strung a length of twisted steel wires. Because rubber bricks are soft this twisted wire quickly saws through them.

After the bricks have been cut to a wedge shape they are carefully rubbed down by hand on a large flat stone until they are the exact wedge shape required as indicated by the sheet zinc template.

The gauged rubber bricks are built to form the arch with joints between the bricks usually 1.5 mm thick. A mortar of sand and lime, or cement, is too coarse for so narrow a joint and the mortar used between the gauged bricks is composed of lime and water. The finished effect of accurately gauged red bricks with thin white joints between them is very attractive.

The three most commonly used brick arch shapes are the semi-circular, the segmental and the flat camber arch. There follows a description of each in detail.

Semi-circular brick arch: Rough (uncut), axed or gauged brick voussoirs may be used to form this arch. Which sort of voussoirs is used will depend upon the quality, that is cost, of the brickwork in which the arch is formed. Rough voussoirs are used mainly for large spans such as railway arches supporting a viaduct or for rear elevations of buildings. Axed voussoirs will generally be used for arches in the main elevations of brick walls built of one of the harder coarser grained facing bricks. Gauged voussoirs are generally used for arches in the main elevations of brick walls built of specially selected fine grained facing bricks.

Brick voussoirs, whether they be rough, axed or gauged, can be laid so that either their stretcher or their header face is exposed. Usually semi-circular arches are formed with bricks showing header faces to avoid the excessively broad wedge-shaped voussoirs or joints that occur with stretcher faces showing. This is illustrated by the comparison of two arches of similar span first with stretcher face showing and then with header face showing, Fig. 95. If the span of the arch is of any considerable width, say 1.8 or more, it is often the practice to build it with what is termed two or more *rings* of bricks as in Fig. 95. An arch with two rings of bricks is stronger in supporting the weight of the brickwork above than one of only one ring, and generally the wider the span, the more rings. One or more rings may be used whether the bricks are rough, axed or gauged.

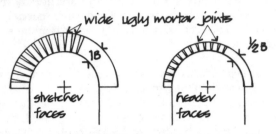

Semi-circular arches with rough voussoirs with stretcher faces showing & header faces showing

joints radiate from centre & do not line up

Two ring semi-circular arch

Fig. 95

Segmental arch: The curve of this arch is a segment, that is part of a circle, and the designer of the building can choose any segment of a circle that he thinks suits his design. By trial and error over many years bricklayers have worked out methods of calculating a segment of a circle related to the span of the arch, which gives a pleasant looking shape of arch, and which at the same time is capable of supporting the weight of brickwork over the arch, such that the rise of the arch is 130 for every metre of span of the arch.

Flat camber arch: This is not a true arch as it is not curved and might well be more correctly named flat brick lintel with voussoirs radiating from a centre (Fig. 96).

The bricks from which the arch is built may either be axed or gauged to the shape required so that the joints between the bricks radiate from a common centre and the widths of voussoirs measured horizontally along the top of the arch are the same. This width will be 65 or slightly less so that there are an odd number of voussoirs, the centre one being a key brick.

The centre from which the joints between the bricks radiate is usually determined either by making the skew or slanting surface at the end of the arch 60 degrees to the horizontal or by calculating the top of this skew line as lying, 130 for every metre of span of opening, in along the wall over the springing point.

If the underside or soffit of this arch were made absolutely level it would appear to be sagging slightly at its centre. This is an optical illusion and it is allowed for by forming a slight rise or camber on the soffit of the arch. This rise is usually calculated at 6 or 10 for every metre of span and the camber takes the form of a shallow curve.

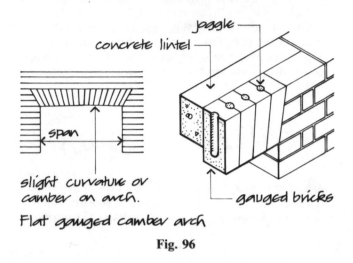

slight curvature or camber on arch.

Flat gauged camber arch

Fig. 96

The camber is allowed for when cutting the bricks to shape. In walls built of hard coarse grained facing bricks this arch is usually built of axed bricks. In walls built of softer fine grained facing bricks the arch is usually of gauged rubber bricks and is termed a flat gauged camber arch. This flat arch must be of such height on face that it bonds in with the brick course of the main walling. The voussoirs of this arch, particularly those at the extreme ends, are often longer overall than a normal brick and the voussoirs have to be formed with two bricks cut to shape.

Flat gauged camber arch: The bricks in this arch are jointed with lime and water, and the joints are usually 1.5 mm thick. As has been said before, lime is soluble in water and does not adhere strongly to bricks as does cement. In time the jointing material, that is lime, between the bricks in this arch may perish and the bricks may slip out of position. To prevent this, joggles are formed between the bricks. These joggles take the form of semi-circular grooves cut in both bed faces of each brick as shown in Fig. 96.

When the bricks are built as an arch there are roughly circular holes between all the bricks and into these holes a wet mix of cement and sand is poured. This hardens and successfully prevents the bricks from slipping out of position. A view of the arch to illustrate the joggles is shown in Fig. 96.

TIMBER

The word timber describes wood which has been cut for use in building. Timber has many advantages as a building material. It is a lightweight material that is easy to cut, shape and join by relatively cheap and simple hand or power operated tools in the production of either a single or a series of wall, floor and roof panels and frames, timber joist, stud, rafter and plate walls, floors and roofs and windows, doors and joinery generally. As a structural material it has favourable weight to cost, weight to strength and weight to modulus of elasticity ratios and coefficients of thermal expansion, K values, density and specific heat. With sensible selection, fabrication and fixing and adequate impregnation or protection it is a reasonably durable material in relation to the life of most buildings. Wood burns at temperatures of about 350°C and chars, the charred outer faces of the wood protecting the unburnt inner wood for periods adequate for escape during fires, in most buildings.

In this age of what the layman calls 'plastics' and 'synthetic' materials some people remark that timber is old-fashioned and suggest that more modern materials such as reinforced concrete should be used for floors and roofs. At present the cost of a timber upper floor for a house is about half that of a similar reinforced concrete floor and as the timber floor is quite adequate for its purpose it seems senseless to double the cost of the floor just to be what is called modern. Much of the timber used in buildings today is cut from the wood of what are called 'conifers'. A coniferous tree is one which has thin needle-like leaves that remain green all year round and whose fruit is carried in woody cones. Examples of this type of tree are fir and pine.

In North America and Europe are very extensive forests of coniferous trees, the wood from which can be economically cut and transported. The wood of coniferous trees is generally less hard than that of other sorts of trees, for example oak, and the wood from all conifers is classified as *soft wood*, whilst the wood from all other trees which have broad leaves is termed *hard wood*.

The cost of a typical soft wood used today is about half that of a typical hard wood.

Softwood is made up of many very thin long cells with their long axis along the length of the trunk or branch. These cells are known as tracheids and they give softwood its strength and texture, and serve to convey sap. The structure of hardwood is more complicated and in most hardwoods the bulk of the wood consists of long fibres. In addition to the fibres there are long cells, called vessels, which conduct water from the roots of the tree to its crown.

Trees whose wood is used for building are all *exogens*, meaning growing outwards, as each year most of these trees form new layers of wood under the bark. Beneath the protective bark around tree trunks and branches is a slimy light green skin. This is termed the cambium and it consists of a layer of wood cells which begin each spring to divide several times to form a layer of new wood cells. All these new wood cells are formed inside the cambium

and the first wood cells formed each year are termed spring wood, and the cells formed later are termed summer wood. The wood cells which are formed first are thinner walled than those formed in the summer and in any cross section cut of wood there are distinct circular rings of light coloured spring wood then darker coloured and thinner rings of summer wood. As a new spring and summer ring is formed each year they are called annual rings, which are shown in Fig. 97.

In the diagram are shown a number of irregular radial lines marked medullary rays. These rays consist of specialised wood cells whose main purpose is to store food in readiness for it to be conveyed to any part of the tree that may require it.

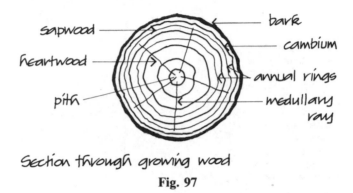

Section through growing wood

Fig. 97

Seasoning of timber

Up to two thirds of the weight of growing wood is due to water in the cells of the wood. When the tree is felled and the wood is cut into timber this water begins to evaporate to the air around the timber, and the wood gradually shrinks as water is removed from the cell walls. As the shrinkage in timber is not uniform the timber may lose shape and it is said to warp. It is essential that before timber is used in buildings, either it should be stacked for a sufficient time in the open air for most of the water in it to dry out, or it should be artificially dried out. If wet timber is used in building it will dry out and shrink and cause cracking of plaster and twisting of doors and windows. The process of allowing, or causing, newly cut wood to dry out is called seasoning, and timber which is ready for use in building is said to have been properly seasoned.

Moisture content of timber: The amount of water in wood varies, and it is not sufficient to allow all timber to dry out for some specific length of time, as one piece of timber may well be seasoned and dried out, whilst another similar piece stacked for the same length of time may still be too wet to use immediately. It is necessary to specify that there shall be a certain amount of water, and no more or less, in timber suitable for building. It is said that timber shall have a certain moisture content, and the moisture content is stated as a percentage of the dry weight of the timber. The dry weight of any piece of timber is its weight after it has been so dried that further drying causes it to lose no more weight. This dry weight is reasonably constant for a given cubic measure of each type of wood and is used as the constant against which the moisture content can be assessed. Table 9 sets out moisture contents for timber.

The moisture content of timber should be such that the timber will not appreciably gain or lose moisture in the position in which it is fixed in a building.

Table 9   Moisture Content of Timber

Position of timber in building	Average moisture content attained in use in a dried-out building (per cent of dry weight)	Moisture content which should not be exceeded at time of erection (per cent of dry weight)
Framing and sheathing of timber buildings (not prefabricated)	16	22
Timber for pre-fabricated buildings	16	17 for precision work, otherwise 22
Rafters and roof boarding, tiling battens, etc.	15	22
Ground floor joists	18	22
Upper floor joists	15	22

Taken from CP 112: Part 2: 1971

Natural dry seasoning: When logs have been cut into timber it is stacked either in the open or in a rough open sided shed. The timbers are stacked with battens between them to allow air to circulate around them. The timbers are left stacked for a year or more, until most of the moisture in the wood has evaporated. Softwoods have to be stacked for a year or two before they are sufficiently dried out or seasoned, and hardwoods for up to ten years. The least moisture content of timber that can be achieved by this method of seasoning is about 18%.

Artificial or kiln seasoning: Because of the great length of time required for natural dry seasoning and because sufficiently low moisture contents of wood cannot be achieved, artificial seasoning is largely used today. After the wood has been converted to timber it is stacked with battens between the timbers and they are then placed in an enclosed kiln. Air is blown through the kiln, the temperature and humidity of the air being regulated to effect seasoning more rapidly than with natural seasoning, but not so rapidly as to cause damage to the timber. If the timber is seasoned too quickly by this process it shrinks and is liable to crack and lose shape badly. To avoid this it is common practice to allow timber to season naturally for a time and then complete the process artificially as described.

Conversion of wood into timber

The method of cutting a log into timber will depend on the ultimate use of the timber.

Most large softwood logs are converted into timbers of different sizes so that there is the least wastage of wood. Smaller softwood logs are usually converted into a few long rectangular section timbers. Most hardwood today is converted into boards.

The method of converting wood to timber affects the timber in two ways: (a) by the change of shape of the timber during seasoning and (b) in the texture and differences in colour on the surface of the wood. Because the spring wood is less dense than the summer wood the shrinkage caused when wood is seasoned (dried) occurs mainly along the line of the annual rings. The circumferential shrinkage is greater than the radial shrinkage. Because of this the shrinkage of one piece of timber cut from a log may be quite different from that cut from another part of the log. This can be illustrated by showing what happens to the planks of a log converted by the 'through and through' cut method shown in Fig. 98. When the planks have been thoroughly seasoned their deformation due to shrinkage can be compared by putting them together in the order in which they were cut from the log as in Fig. 98. From this it will be seen that the plank which was cut with its long axis on the radius of the circle of the log lost shape least noticeably and was the best timber after seasoning.

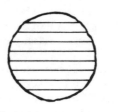 

Log through and through sawn

Deformation of planks due to shrinkage

Fig. 98

It is apparent that timber which is required to retain its shape during seasoning, such as good quality boarding, must somehow be cut as nearly as possible along the radius of the centre of the log. As it is not practicable to cut a log in the way we cut a slice out of an apple, logs which are to be cut along their radius are first cut into quarters. Each quarter of the log is then cut into boards or planks. This can be done in a variety of ways. Two of the most economical ways of doing this are shown here in Fig. 99. It will be seen from these diagrams that one or two boards or planks are cut very near a radius of the circle whilst the rest are cut somewhat off the radius and the former will lose shape least. In describing the structure and growth of a tree the medullary rays were described as being narrow radial lines of wood cells of different shape and structure than the main wood cell.

If the face of a timber is cut on a radius of the circle of the log, the cells of the medullary rays may be exposed where the cut is made. With many woods this produces a very pleasing texture and colour on the surface of the wood and it is said that the 'figure' of the wood has been exposed. To expose the figure of wood by cutting along the medullary rays a quarter of a log has to be very wastefully cut as shown in Fig. 100. The radial cutting of boards as shown is very expensive and is employed only for high-class cabinet making and panelling timbers where the exposed figure of the wood will be used decoratively.

Log quartered & converted into boards

Fig. 99

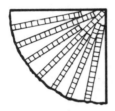

radial sawn boards

Fig. 100

Stress grading of timber

There is an appreciable variation in the actual strength of similar pieces of timber which had led in the past to very conservative design in the use of timber as a structural material. Uncertain of the strength of individual timbers, it was practice to overdesign, that is, make allowance for the possibility of weakness in a timber and so select timbers larger than necessary.

Of recent years, systems of stress grading have been adopted with the result that a more certain design approach is possible with a reduction of up to 25% in the section of structural timbers. Stress grading of structural timbers, which was first adopted in The Building Regulations 1972, is now generally accepted in selecting building timber.

There are two methods of stress grading: visual grading and machine grading.

Visual grading: Trained graders determine the grade of a timber by a visual examination from which they assess the effect on strength of observed defects such as knots, shakes, wane and slope of grain. There are two visual grades, General Structural (GS) and Special Structural (SS), the allowable stress in SS being higher than in GS.

Machine grading: Timbers are subjected to a test for stiffness by measuring deflection under load in a machine which applies a specified load across overlapping metre lengths to determine the stress grade. This mechanical test, which is based on the fact that strength is proportional to stiffness, is a more certain assessment of the true strength of a timber than a visual test. The machine grades, which are comparable to the visual grades, are Machine General Structural (MGS) and Machine Special Structural (MSS). There are in addition two further machine grades, M50 and M75.

Stress graded timbers are marked GS and SS at least once within the length of each piece for visually graded timber together with a mark to indicate the grader or company. Machine graded timber is likewise marked MGS, M50, MSS and M75 together with the BS kitemark and the number of the British Standard, 4978.

Schedule 6 of The Building Regulations 1976, tables maximum spans of structural timbers in relation to spacing, dead load, size of timber and stress grading. In the Schedule GS, MGS, M50 and M75 are comparable and SS and MSS are comparable.

Decay in timber

Fungal decay: Any one of a number of wood-destroying fungi may attack timber that is persistently wet and has moisture content of over 20%.

Dry rot: This is the most serious form of fungal decay and is caused by *Seupula lacrymans* which can spread and cause extensive destruction of timber. The description dry rot derives from the fact that timber which has been attacked appears dry and powdery.

The airborne spores of this fungus settle on timber and if its moisture content is greater than 20% they germinate. (If the wood has less moisture content than 20% germination does not occur.) The spore forms long thread-like cells which pierce the wood cells and use the wood as a food. The thread-like cells multiply, spreading out long white thread-like arms called mycelium which feed on other wood cells. This fungus can spread many tens of feet from the point where the spore first began to thrive, and is capable of forming thick greyish strands which can find their way through lime mortar and the softer bricks.

Timber which is affected by this fungus turns dark brown and shrinks and dries into a cracked powdery dry mass which looks as though it has been charred by fire.

Prevention of dry rot: Never use unseasoned timber in buildings. Prevent seasoned timber becoming so wet that it can support the fungus by:

(a) building in a good horizontal damp-proof course;
(b) either ventilating the space below or around timber floors or by designing the building so that these spaces do not become damp;
(c) immediately repairing all leaking water, rain water

and drain pipes which otherwise might saturate timber to such an extent as to make it liable to dry rot.

Repair and renewal of timbers affected by dry rot: Every bit of timber which has been affected by the fungus or is in close proximity to it must be taken out or cut out of the building, and this timber should be burnt immediately. The purpose of burning the affected timber is to ensure that none of it is used in the repairs and to kill any spore that might cause further rot.

All walls on which, or against which, the fungus grew must be thoroughly cleaned and sterilised by application of a fungicidal solution. Any old lime plaster on which or through which the rot has spread should be hacked off and renewed in a cement plaster. New timber used to replace affected timber should be treated with a wood preservative before it is fixed or built in.

Wet rot is caused principally by *Coniophora puteana*, the cellar fungus, which occurs more frequently, but is less serious, than dry rot. Decay of timber due to wet rot is confined to timber that is in damp situations such as cellars, ground floors without damp-proof courses and roofs. The rot causes darkening and longitudinal cracking of timber and there is often little or no visible growth of fungus on the surface of timber.

Prevention of wet rot: Timber should not be built into or in contact with any part of the structure that is likely to remain damp. Damp-proof courses and damp-proof membranes above and at ground level and sensibly detailed flashings and gutters to roofs and chimneys will prevent the conditions suited to the growth of wet rot fungus.

Repair and renewal of timbers affected by wet rot: Affected timber must be cut out and replaced by sound new timber treated with a preservative. It is not necessary to sterilise brickwork around the area of affected timber.

Insect attack on wood

In this country the three sorts of insects which most commonly cause damage to timber are the furniture beetle, the death-watch beetle and the house longhorn beetle. The common furniture beetle (*Anobium punctatum*) is the beetle whose larvae most commonly attack timber and furniture and its attack is generally known as 'wood worm'. Between June and August the beetles fly around and after mating the female lays small eggs in the cracks and crevices of any dry softwood or hardwood. The eggs hatch and a small white grub emerges. These grubs (larvae) have powerful biting jaws with which they tunnel into the wood, using the wood as food. The grubs tunnel along the grain of the wood for a year or two until they are fully grown, then they bore to just below the surface of the wood where they pupate or, change into beetles. These emerge in June to August and the life cycle of the beetle is repeated. The hole which each grub makes is very small and timber is structurally weakened only if a great number of these holes tunnelled by a number of grubs are formed over many years. The holes are very unsightly, particularly if the beetle infests furniture or panelling.

The death-watch beetle (*Xestobium rufovillosum*): The grubs of this beetle thrive particularly well on very old timbers that have suffered decay and rarely attack softwoods. The beetle lays eggs which hatch into grubs (larvae) which, in turn, do as the larvae of the furniture beetle, tunnel along the wood for from one to several years. The name death-watch beetle derives from the ticking sound made by the beetles as they tap their heads on timber during the mating season in May and June. Again only after years of infestation by this beetle is the strength of timber seriously affected.

House longhorn beetle (*Hylotrupes bajulus*): A large insect that has in recent years been active in London and the home counties, that attacks mainly softwood. It has a life cycle of up to 11 years and can cause such extensive damage that only a thin shell of sound timber is left. There is little external evidence of the infestation except some unevenness of wood surfaces due to borings just below the surface. The Building Regulations 1976 specifies areas of the south of England in which the softwood timbers of roofs are required to be treated with a suitable preservative against attack by the longhorn beetle.

The powder-post beetle: The larvae of this beetle only attack hardwoods stored in timber yards. The name derives from the powder found at the foot of hardwood posts stored in timber yards.

Control of attacks by beetles: Timber which has been affected by the larvae of these beetles should be sprayed or painted with a proprietary preservative during early summer and autumn. These preservatives prevent the larvae changing to beetles at the surface of the wood and so arrest further infestation.

Wood preservation

Timber is treated with preservatives to protect it against damage by fungi and insects. Wood preservatives are divided into three main groups:

(a) tar oils
(b) water-borne
(c) organic solvent.

Tar oil preservatives are blends of distillate oils of coal tar, commonly known as creosote. Bethell's Patent for coal tar creosote (taken out in 1838) is still widely used today as a preservative for railway sleepers, posts, farm buildings and fences. Creosote reduces moisture absorption and is a very effective protection against fungal and insect attack. It is a brown viscous liquid which has a strong odour and that cannot be painted over. It is extensively used to preserve timbers used externally, where appearance is not a consideration.

Timber should be adequately seasoned before treatment with a preservative. Creosote may be painted and sprayed on surfaces to give protection to the depth of the penetration of the liquid below surface. Timbers steeped or immersed in creosote are protected to the extent of the penetration of the creosote which is a product of the nature of the wood and the length of time of immersion. Pressure impregnation is the most effective method of preservation. There are two methods of impregnation, the full cell and the empty cell process. In the full cell process timbers are sealed in a vacuum cylinder in which air is removed from the wood cells which are then filled with creosote under pressure to give full protection of all the cells of the timber. In the empty cell process creosote is introduced under pressure after the timbers have been subjected to pressure and then surplus creosote is withdrawn by vacuum so that all the wood cells are given adequate protection. This latter process, which uses less creosote, is less likely to cause bleeding of creosote from the surface than the full cell process.

Water-borne preservatives: The two types of preservative used, boron compounds for green (not seasoned) timber and combinations of copper, chrome and arsenic (C.C.A.) for seasoned timber are both water soluble. The C.C.A. preservatives are usually used to pressure impregnate timbers which after treatment have high resistance to attack by fungi and insects. The C.C.A. water-borne preservative is commonly used for structural timbers liable to attack. The preservative gives light coloured wood a light grey/green colour and is liable to cause some slight swelling of timber.

Organic solvent type preservatives: These preservatives contain fungicidal and/or insecticidal ingredients of low water solubility that are dissolved in volatile solvents such as white spirit that evaporate, leaving the fungicide and insecticide in the wood. These preservatives do not cause any change in moisture content or dimension in wood and are particularly suitable for joinery timbers. They are non-corrosive to metals and can be satisfactorily over painted. Pressure impregnation is the most effective method of using these preservatives.

Finishes for timber

There are three types of finish for wood, paint, varnish and stains. The traditional finishes paint and varnish are protective and decorative finishes which afford some protection against water externally and provide a decorative finish which can easily be cleaned internally. Paints are opaque and hide the surfaces of the wood whereas varnishes are sufficiently transparent for the texture and grain of the wood to show. Of recent years stains have been much used on timber externally. There is a wide range of stains available, from those that leave a definite film on the surface to those that penetrate the surface and range from gloss through semi-gloss to matt finish. The purpose of this finish is to give a selected uniform colour to wood without masking the grain and texture of the wood. Most stains contain a preservative to inhibit fungal surface growth. These stains are most effective on rough sawn timbers.

Fire resistance of wood

The resistance of timber to damage by fire varies enormously and depends on the size of the timber and the sort of wood from which it was cut. Large timbers can withstand exposure to intense flame for days without losing appreciable strength. The timbers char but do not burn. Small timbers such as boards and battens particularly of dry softwood burn easily. Many hardwoods are particularly difficult to burn and have to be cut to small size and thoroughly dried before they will even begin to burn.

There are many instances of the resistance to fire of timbers of large section where, in a building damaged by extensive fire, steel has buckled and collapsed, reinforced concrete has failed but large timbers have safely withstood the effects of fire.

There are fire-retardant materials available which will delay the ignition and spread of flame on the surface of timbers in a fire. There are two types, the water-soluble which is applied by pressure impregnation and surface coatings. Water-soluble salts and water-soluble resins are pressure impregnated into timbers and considerably improve resistance to damage by fire. Surface coatings, such as intumescent phosphate resin, considerably improve the resistance to spread of flame.

Timber walls

The construction of a timber framed wall is a rapid, clean, dry operation. The timbers can be cut and assembled with simple hand or power operated tools and once the wall is raised into position and fixed it is ready to receive wall finishes. A timber framed wall has adequate stability and strength to support the floors and roof of small buildings, such as houses. Covered with wall finishes it has sufficient resistance to damage by fire, good thermal insulating properties and reasonable durability providing it is sensibly constructed and protected from decay.

In North America timber is as commonly used for walls as brick is in the United Kingdom. A timber framed house can be constructed on site by two men in a matter of a few days. There has been a prejudice against timber buildings in this country for a long time based mainly on the misconception of the fire hazard of timber as a structural material. With changing fashion and a more realistic acceptance of the properties and advantages of timber as a structural material it is becoming more widely used as the frame for houses and as non-loadbearing panel walling for cross wall construction.

Timber framed walls consist of small section timbers fixed vertically at centres to suit the loads to be supported and materials to be used as weathering and facing, fixed to a bottom and a top member to form the traditional timber stud frame illustrated in Fig. 101, which derives its name from the vertical members called studs. The bottom and top members, termed sole (or cill) and head plate respectively, are of the same section of timber as the studs. Figure 101 is an illustration of a typical timber stud frame suitable for both external and internal walls and loadbearing and non-loadbearing walls. Fixed between loadbearing cross walls as the front or back wall of a terrace house or fixed internally between brick or block walls, this simple stud frame has adequate stability and needs no additional bracing.

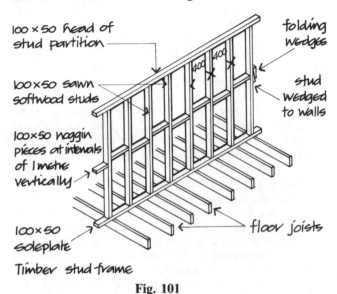

100 × 50 head of stud partition

100 × 50 sawn softwood studs

100 × 50 noggin pieces at intervals of 1 metre vertically

100 × 50 soleplate

folding wedges

stud wedged to walls

floor joists

Timber stud frame

Fig. 101

The simple timber stud wall, with the vertical studs nailed to the sole and head plates, does not in itself have sufficient stability or rigidity to be used for the walls of buildings because the non-rigid connection of the members of the frame will not strongly resist racking due to lateral forces such as wind and eccentric loading. The timber stud wall has, therefore, to be braced against racking if it is to be used as a freestanding timber frame. Bracing may be provided by diagonal timber braces built into the frame or a wall covering of diagonal boarding or plywood can be used to provide sufficient rigidity. Practice today is to use the sheathing of boards or plywood as bracing.

The small lightweight sections of timber used lend themselves to a system of prefabrication either on site or off. Practice is to assemble stud frames on a floor or bench and then to manhandle them into position on site. The simplest way of assembling or prefabricating timber stud walls is to construct wall or storey height frames that can be raised into position without heavy lifting gear.

Platform frame: Wall frames of the height between structural floor and ceilings are assembled and raised into position on a prepared base. The upper floor joists are fixed across the head of the frames and the floor is covered with boards to form a level platform off which the frames of the next floor can be erected as illustrated in Fig. 102,

hence the name platform frame. The advantage of this platform frame system of erection is simplicity and speed of erection, convenience in working from a level platform and the stiffening effect of the floor between frames. This system of framing depends on the stud frames being stiffened with a sheathing of plywood or diagonal boards to provide rigidity in handling, erection and in use. The header nailed to the ends of the floor joists serves to seal the cavities between joists for insulation and as a fixing for external finishes.

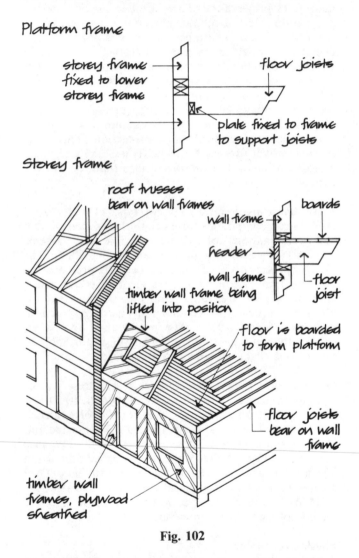

Platform frame

storey frame fixed to lower storey frame

floor joists

plate fixed to frame to support joists

Storey frame

roof trusses bear on wall frames

wall frame

boards

header

wall frame

floor joist

timber wall frame being lifted into position

floor is boarded to form platform

floor joists bear on wall frame

timber wall frames, plywood sheathed

Fig. 102

Storey frames: Wall frames of storey height, that is the height between floors, are assembled, raised and fixed to a prepared base. Upper floor joists are fixed to a plate fixed to the studs and the next wall frame is raised and fixed directly on top of the lower frame as illustrated in Fig. 102. This system of stud framing and assembly is particularly suited to frames that are assembled with the external weathering of boards in place so that either an overlap or a weathering strip will complete the joint between frames.

The advantages of the platform and storey frames are flexibility in positioning openings between one storey and another, the comparatively short lengths of timber minimise warping due to drying shrinkage and these lightweight panels can be manhandled. A timber framed wall may be assembled in two or more panels for ease of handling and erection. The panels are lifted into position and secured to a continuous separate head plate and a separate continuous sole plate.

Balloon frame is a two storey stud frame assembled either on or off site and raised into position. The upper floor joists are fixed on a plate or ledger and nailed to the sides of the studs as illustrated in Fig. 103. The roof is fixed and covered so that subsequent building operations are under cover. A balloon frame panel is particularly suited for use as a side wall of a two storey timber framed building with the end walls of platform or storey frames to support the upper floor and roof. The disadvantage of a balloon frame is its size for transport and handling, the long lengths of stud which may twist due to drying shrinkage and the limitation on choice of position of openings due to the continuous studs.

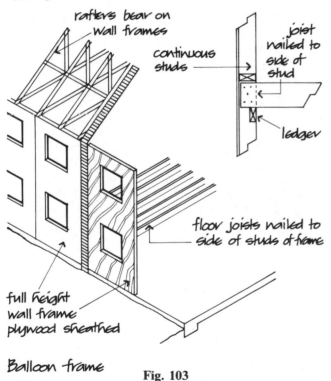

Balloon frame

Fig. 103

Foundation: Timber wall frames are erected on a foundation of conventional walls or a concrete base or raft to which a sole plate is bolted as illustrated in Fig. 104. The sole plate is bedded on a d.p.c. Where a wall is assembled as one frame, the sole of the frame may be bolted direct to the foundation. Where the wall is made up of two or more frames then a separate sole plate is first bolted to the foundation and the separate frames are nailed to it.

Angles and intersections: To provide a secure fixing for internal and external finishes and as a means of fixing frames at angles and intersections it is usual to use an additional stud as illustrated in Fig. 104.

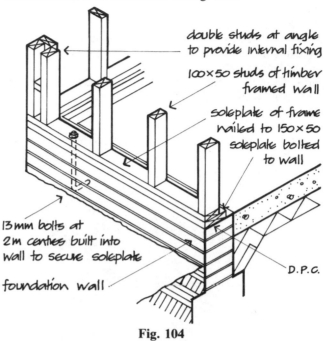

Fig. 104

Openings for windows and doors are framed with either single or double head and cill timbers depending on the width of the opening, single members for narrow and double for wide as illustrated in Fig. 105.

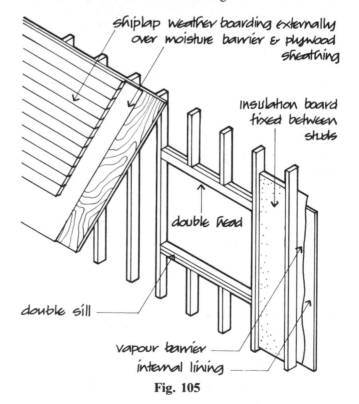

Fig. 105

External and internal finishes and linings: One of the advantages of a timber frame as a wall is that it is a dry form of construction and it is sensible, therefore, to use systems of dry finishes and linings, such as plasterboard and boards.

The combination of a timber stud frame wall and its finishes will not provide sufficient thermal insulation so that it is necessary to use some insulating material fixed either between the studs or over the inside face of the wall. To prevent moisture from the warm air side of the wall penetrating the insulation it is necessary to fix a vapour barrier between the inside of the building and the insulation as illustrated in Fig. 105. It will be seen that the external weather boarding is fixed to the plywood sheathing over a moisture barrier of waterproof paper.

The plywood facing acts to brace the frame and the moisture barrier against penetration of rain.

External weatherings of boarding, vertical tiling and slating are the traditional materials used as weathering for timber framed external walls, either singly or in combination. Boarding has the advantage of being light-weight but requires protection against decay by preservatives or painting, whereas tiling and slating are comparatively heavy but require no maintenance.

A timber framed wall may be used as the inner skin of a cavity wall with a brick outer skin. Here the advantage of the durability and appearance of brick are combined with the lightweight, dry construction of a timber frame.

CHAPTER THREE

FLOORS

Up to the nineteenth century the ground floors of most small buildings were formed directly off the ground, the soil being rammed until it was firm and on it were laid flagstones or bricks to form a hard surface. This sort of floor was unsatisfactory, because the moisture which was continuously withdrawn from the soil below the building made the floor damp and cold, and a great deal of heat was required to dry out the damp air in the ground floor rooms. During the nineteenth and early years of the twentieth centuries, when many of the central town and city dwellings were built, it was common practice to construct the ground floor of timber, raised above the level of the ground inside the building. This type of floor is called a raised ground floor and its great advantage is that the space between the raised timber ground floor and the earth below prevents much dampness from rising to the floor above. Because of the unhealthy conditions in which many people lived, due to dampness from floors formed directly off the ground, the first Model Health Byelaws, 1936 required all inhabited buildings, built after that date, to have a continuous layer of concrete spread between the external walls of the building to prevent dampness rising from the ground into the building. This layer of concrete spread over the site of the building had to be 150 thick. Some years after the Second World War, the acute shortage of timber in this country and later the sharp increase in building costs made it either impossible, or at the best very expensive, to construct raised timber ground floors and the solid ground floor came into common use. This is a floor formed directly off the site concrete which is surfaced with some hard, smooth, attractive floor finish.

Functional requirements

The functional requirements of a floor are:

Stability
Strength
Prevention of passage of moisture
Durability
Fire resistance
Thermal properties
Resistance to sound transmission and sound absorption.

Stability: A floor is designed and constructed to serve as a horizontal surface to support people and their furniture, equipment or machinery. The floor should have adequate stiffness to remain reasonably stable and horizontal under the dead load of the floor structure and such partitions and other fixtures it supports and the anticipated static and live loads it is designed to support. The floor structure should also support and accommodate either in its depth, or below or above, electrical, water, heating and ventilating services without affecting its stability. For stability there should be adequate vertical support for the floor structure and the floor should have adequate stiffness against gross deflection under load.

Solid ground and basement floors are usually built off the ground from which they derive support. The stability of such floors depends, therefore, on the characteristics of the hardcore and soil under them. For small domestic loads the site concrete, without reinforcement, provides adequate stability. For heavier loads, such as heavy equipment or machinery, a reinforced concrete slab is generally necessary with, in addition, a separate pile foundation under heavy machinery.

On shrinkable clay soils it may be necessary to reinforce the oversite concrete slab against differential expansion or contraction of the soil, especially where there are deep rooted trees near the building.

Upper or suspended floors are supported by walls or beams and should have adequate stiffness to minimise deflection under load. Under load a floor will deflect and bend and this deflection or bending should be limited to avoid cracking of rigid finishes such as plasterboard and to avoid the sense of apprehension in those below the floor that they might suffer, if the deflection or bending were obvious. A deflection of about 1/300 of the span is generally accepted as a maximum in the design of floors.

Strength: The strength of a floor depends on the characteristics of the materials used for the structure of the floor, such as timber, steel or concrete. The floor structure must be strong enough to safely support the dead load of the floor and its finishes, fixtures, partitions and services and the anticipated imposed loads. Dead loads are calculated from the unit weight of the materials set out in BS 648 and imposed loads from the tables in The Building Regulations 1976. From these calculations the required strength of the floor is determined. Where imposed loads are small, as in domestic buildings, the timber floor construction may be determined from the span of the floor and the imposed loads set out in Schedule 6 of The Building Regulations 1976.

Prevention of passage of moisture: The ground floor of a building, especially a heated building, will tend to encourage moisture from the ground below to rise and make the floor damp and feel cold and uncomfortable. This in turn may require additional heating to provide reasonable conditions of comfort. An appreciable transfer of moisture from the ground to the floor may promote conditions favourable to wood rot and so cause damage to timber ground floors and finishes. Obviously the degree of penetration of moisture from the ground to a floor will depend on the nature of the subsoil, the water table and whether the site is level or sloping. On a gravel or coarse grained sand base, where the water table throughout the year is well below the surface, there will be little penetration whereas on a clay base, with the water table close to the surface, there will be appreciable penetration of moisture from the ground to floors. In the former instance a concrete slab alone will be a sufficient barrier and in the latter a waterproof membrane on, in or under the concrete slab will be necessary to prevent moisture rising to the surface of the floor. The Building Regulations 1976 require ground floors to be so constructed to prevent the passage of moisture to the surface of the floor. Deemed-to-satisfy provisions for a raised timber ground floor are 100 site contrete on a bed of hardcore with a space of at least 75 between the top of the concrete and the wall plate and 125 to the underside of suspended timbers as illustrated in Fig. 106. Deemed-to-satisfy provisions for a solid ground floor incorporating timber are 100 of site concrete, hardcore and a damp-proof membrane.

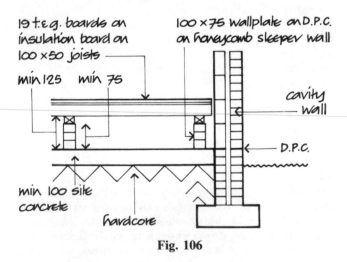

Fig. 106

Durability: Ground floors on a solid base protected against rising moisture from the ground, and suspended upper floors solidly supported and adequately constructed and protected inside a sound envelope of walls and roof, should be durable for the expected life of the building and require little maintenance or repair.

Fire resistance: Suspended upper floors should be so constructed to provide resistance to fire for a period adequate for the escape of the occupants from the building. The notional periods of resistance to fire, from $\frac{1}{2}$ to 6 hours, depending on the size and use of the building, are set out in The Building Regulations. In general a timber floor provides a lesser period of resistance to fire than a reinforced concrete floor. In consequence timber floors will provide adequate resistance to fire in small domestic buildings, and concrete floors the longer periods of resistance to fire required in large buildings, where required periods of resistance are high.

Thermal properties: A floor should provide resistance to transfer of heat where there is normally significant air temperature difference on the opposite sides of the floor. Obviously a ground floor should be constructed to minimise transfer of heat from the building to the ground or the ground to the building. Both hardcore and a damp-proof membrane on, under or sandwiched in the oversite concrete will assist in preventing the floor being damp and feeling cold and so reduce heating required for comfort and reduce transfer of heat. Where under floor heating is used it is essential to introduce a layer of insulation below and around the edges of the floor slab to reduce transfer of heat to the ground.

Where there is likely to be appreciable heat loss through a floor, as there is with a ventilated raised timber ground floor, then the floor should be insulated against excessive transfer of heat.

Resistance to sound transmission and sound absorption: Upper floors that separate dwellings, or separate noisy from quiet activities, should act as a barrier to the transmission of airborne sound and reduce impact sound. The comparatively low mass of a timber floor will transmit airborne sound more readily than a high mass concrete floor, so that floors between dwellings, for example, are generally constructed of concrete. The resistance to sound transmission of a timber floor can be improved by filling the spaces between the timber joists with either lightweight insulating material or a dense material. The additional cost of such filling to a new floor for the comparatively small reduction in sound transmission may not be worthwhile where, for a modest increase in cost, a concrete floor will be more effective. Where existing buildings, with timber floors, are to be converted into flats the only reasonable way of improving sound insulation between floors is the use of filling between joists.

The reduction of impact sound is best effected by a floor covering such as carpet that deadens the sound of footsteps on either a timber or a concrete floor.

The hard surfaces of the floor and ceiling of both timber and concrete floors will not appreciably absorb airborne sounds which will be reflected and may build up to an uncomfortable level. The sound absorption of a floor can be improved by carpet or felt, and the ceiling by the use of one of the absorbent 'acoustic' tile or panel finishes.

SOLID GROUND FLOORS

Most ground floors, today, are constructed as solid ground floors with hardcore, oversite concrete and a damp-proof membrane as described in chapter 1, on which a floor finish is usually laid or fixed.

Floor finishes for solid floors

For sheds, workshops, stores and garages, the finished top surface of the oversite concrete is sometimes used as the floor surface to save the cost of an applied floor surface, or finish. Concrete is not satisfactory as a floor surface because even though it can be given a smooth finish with a power float, many of the fine particles of sand and cement are brought to the surface. These particles have poor resistance to wear and in a short time the surface of the concrete 'dusts' and requires frequent vigorous brushing. Being a coarse grained material, concrete cannot be washed and if it becomes stained the stains are permanent.

A concrete floor finished by power floating is generally a satisfactory base for the thicker floor finishes such as mastic asphalt, thick tiles and wood blocks. For the thin finishes such as plastic, linoleum and rubber sheet and tile, the more precisely level, smooth surface of a screeded base is necessary.

Floor screeds: The purpose of a floor screed is to provide a smooth level surface on which a floor finish can be applied. The usual materials for a floor screed are cement, sand and water which are thoroughly mixed, spread over the surface of the concrete base, compacted, levelled and trowelled to a smooth finish. The thickness of the screed and the mix of cement and sand depends on the surface on which the screed is laid. The cement-rich mix used in a screed will shrink as it dries out and the thinner the screed the more rapidly it will dry and the more it will shrink and crack.

A screed laid on a concrete base, within three hours of placing the concrete, will bond strongly to the concrete and dry slowly with the concrete so that drying shrinkage and cracking of the screed will be minimised. For this monolithic construction of screed a thickness of 12 of screed will suffice.

A screed laid on a concrete base that has set and hardened should be at least 40 thick. To provide a good bond between the screed and the concrete, the surface of the concrete should be hacked by mechanical means, cleaned and dampened and then covered by a thin grout of water and cement before the screed is laid. With a good bond to the concrete base a separate screed at least 40 thick will dry sufficiently slowly to avoid serious shinkage cracking.

Where a screed is laid on an impermeable damp-proof membrane there will be no appreciable bond between the screed and the concrete base so that drying shrinkage of the screed is unrestrained. So that the screed does not dry too rapidly and suffer shrinkage cracking, the screed in this unbonded construction should be at least 50 thick.

A screed laid on a layer of compressible thermal or sound insulating material should be at least 65 thick if this floating construction is not to crack due to drying shrinkage and the loads on the floor.

For screeds up to 40 thick, a mix of Portland cement and clean sand in the proportions by weight of 1:3 to $1:4\frac{1}{2}$ is used. The lower the proportion of cement to sand the less the drying shrinkage. For screeds over 40 thick a mix of fine concrete is often used in the proportions of $1:1\frac{1}{2}:3$ of cement, fine aggregate and coarse aggregate with a maximum of 10 for the coarse aggregate.

Screeds should be mixed with just sufficient water for workability. The material is spread over the surface of the base and thoroughly compacted by tamping to the required thickness and level and then is finished with a wood or steel float. A wood float finish is used for wood block and thick tile floors and a steel finish for the thin sheet and tile finishes. The screed should be cured, that is allowed to dry out slowly over the course of several days, by covering it with sheeting, such as polythene, to minimise rapid drying shrinkage and cracking.

There are on the market several screeds designed specifically for use in public places and factories where resistance to wear, freedom from dust, resistance to oils and acids and ease of cleaning are considerations. These screeds of cement rubber-latex, cement bitumen emulsion, cement resin, and resins and binders are spread to a thickness of from 13 to 2 and finished by a trowel on a prepared cement and sand screed for the thin finishes and on a floated concrete base for the thicker materials.

A good floor surface should be smooth, level and sufficiently hard so that it is not worn away for many years. It should not readily absorb water or other liquids likely to be spilled on it and it should be capable of being easily cleaned.

The floor finishes in common use may be classified as:

Jointless
Thin tile and sheet
Wood and wood based
Thick tile

Jointless floor finishes

Granolithic paving: In factories, stores, garages and like buildings, where the floor has to withstand heavy wear, granolithic paving is often used. This consists of a mixture of crushed granite which has been carefully sieved so that the particles are graded from coarse to very fine in such proportions that the material when mixed will be particularly free of voids or small spaces, and when mixed with cement will be a dense mass. The usual proportions of the mix are $2\frac{1}{2}$ of granite chippings to one of Portland cement by volume. These materials are mixed with water and the wet mix is spread uniformly and trowelled to a smooth flat surface. When this paving has dried and hardened it is very hard wearing.

Every material which has a matrix (binding agent) of cement shrinks with quite considerable force as it dries out and hardens. Granolithic paving is rich in cement and when it is spread over site concrete it shrinks as it dries out and hardens. This shrinkage is resisted by the concrete. If the concrete is dense and hard, and its surface has been thoroughly brushed to remove all dust or loose particles, it will successfully restrain the shrinkage in the granolithic paving. If, however, the concrete on which the granolithic paving is spread is of poor quality, or if the surface of the concrete is covered with dust and loose particles, the shrinkage of the granolithic paving will be unrestrained and it will crack and, in time, break up. On good clean concrete which has dried out the granolithic paving is spread to a thickness of about 20 and is trowelled to a smooth surface.

If the granolithic paving is laid as soon as the oversite concrete is hard enough to stand on, then the paving can be spread 15 thick. This at once economises in the use of the granolithic material, which is expensive, and at the same time, because the wet granolithic binds firmly to the still damp concrete, there is very little likelihood of the paving cracking as it dries out. Granolithic paving which is to be spread over old, poor quality concrete, liable to crumble and dust, must be laid at least 65 thick to prevent it cracking seriously as it dries out.

The reason for this is that if the granolithic paving is spread thinly it will dry out very quickly and shrink fiercely. The shrinkage will not be restrained by the poor concrete below and the paving will crack and fall to pieces. If, however, the paving is 65 thick, or more, it will dry out slowly and the shrinkage of the top surface, which dries out first, will be restrained by the wetter material below, which takes longer to dry out, and in this way cracking of the material is avoided.

Because the floor layer (pavior) runs screeds to obtain a true level finish this paving is sometimes described as granolithic screed, or a screed of granolithic. As has been said, the finished surface of granolithic paving is smooth, dense and hard wearing but with very heavy wear the material will break up very slightly in time and form dust. This dust may cause serious damage to some machinery and make working conditions unpleasant. There are on the market a number of preparations which, if added to the granolithic paving material, will considerably reduce the amount of dust caused by wear on the surface of the paving. These proprietary preparations vary considerably in composition and generally have the effect of sealing the minute pores in the material, or of forming a hard, water-repellent skin on the surface. These preparations are variously described as 'sealers' or 'hardeners'. The resistance to wear on the surface of granolithic paving can be improved by sprinkling the surface, whilst it is still wet, with fine carborundum. The carborundum is then trowelled in. Carborundum is very hard and because it is expensive it is applied only as a very thin top dressing.

Mastic asphalt flooring: Mastic asphalt for flooring is made from either limestone aggregate, natural rock or black pitch-mastic in the natural colour of the material or coloured. Mastic asphalt serves both as a floor finish and a damp-proof membrane. It is a smooth, hardwearing, dust free finish, easy to clean but liable to be slippery when wet. The light duty grade is fairly readily indented by furniture. Mastic asphalt has been less used as a floor finish since the advent of the thin plastic tiles and sheets.

The light duty, non-industrial grade, which is laid in one coat to a finished thickness of from 15 to 20, is used for offices, schools and housing. The medium grade is laid in one coat to a thickness of 20 to 25 and the heavy duty in one coat to a thickness of 30 to 50. Mastic asphalt can be laid on a level, power floated concrete finish or on a level, smooth cement and sand screed. The asphalt finish can be coloured in one of the red or brown shades available.

Magnesite floor finish: The finish is composed of burned magnesite, fine sawdust, wood flour and water to which is added some magnesium chloride solution. The proportions of the materials are 9 magnesite, 2 sawdust, 1 wood flour. The magnesium chloride combines with the magnesite to form magnesium oxychloride which hardens and acts as a very hard, strong cement.

The materials are mixed on the site, preferably by machine, and the magnesium chloride is added and mixed in. This forms a mass of putty-like consistency which is spread evenly over the surface to be covered, and is trowelled flat and level. The material gradually hardens and when it is hard enough to stand the weight of a board, with a man on it, the surface is scraped to remove trowel marks and then trowelled again. The surface hardens in about forty-eight hours and is then sealed with a chloride solution. This finish can be laid in one or two coats. One coat is laid to a finished thickness of about 20 and for the two coat work a 15 thick undercoat and 5 finishing coat are laid. The two coat work is used when a grained or mottled surface is required.

The finish can be pigmented to give many different colours among which red and buff are popular. The finished surface can be mottled and grained with various colours in imitation of marble. Magnesite finish can be laid on a clean level concrete floor or on a screed of cement and sand. This floor finish is hard and resistant to normal wear on domestic and office floors. It does not crack or powder, if properly laid, and being resistant to water, mineral oils and fats can be washed and if oiled is easily kept clean.

Magnesite floor finish can only be successfully laid by craftsmen trained in the use of the materials. Of late years this finish has lost popularity because it has been given a bad name due to serious failures of the surface finishes when laid by men not competent in the use of the materials.

Thin tile and sheet materials

Plastic floor finishes: Thin tiles and sheets of plastic are much used as floor finishes for offices, schools and public buildings because of low initial cost and ease of cleaning. The materials available are:

Thermoplastic tiles
PVC (vinyl) asbestos tiles
Flexible PVC tiles and sheets
Flexible PVC sheets on a backing of felt or cellular PVC.

Thermoplastic tiles are made from a blend of mineral asphalt and/or thermoplastic resins, such as those obtained from the distillation of coal or oil, asbestos fibres, fillers and pigments. The standard size of tile is 300 and 250 square in thicknesses of 2.5 mm and 3.0 mm. The standard tile is used in offices and schools where grease and oil, which may cause deterioration, are not present. The tiles are not as flexible for laying as other plastic materials and are somewhat hard and noisy underfoot.

Thermoplastic tiles – PVC modified, have better resistance to grease and oil and are slightly more flexible than the standard grade.

PVC (vinyl) asbestos tiles, sometimes termed vinyl tiles or asbestos tiles, are made from a blend of thermoplastic binder (either vinyl chloride polymer or vinyl chloride copolymer or both), asbestos fibres, fillers and pigment in sizes of 225 and 300 square and thicknesses of 1.6, 2.0, 2.5, 3.0 and 3.2 mm. These tiles have better resistance to grease and oil than thermoplastic tiles, have only moderate flexibility and are somewhat hard and noisy underfoot.

Flexible PVC tiles and sheets are made from a blend of thermoplastic binder (either vinyl chloride polymer or vinly chloride copolymer or both), fillers and pigments in tiles 225, 250 and 300 square and sheets 1.2, 1.5, 1.8, 2.0 and 2.1 m wide and thicknesses of 1.5, 2.0 and 3.0 mm. Because of their flexibility these tiles and sheets are easier to lay than PVC asbestos tiles and having a brighter clearer colour are often preferred.

Flexible PVC sheets with a backing are made from a blend of polymeric materials (either vinyl chloride polymer or vinyl chloride copolymer or both), with fillers and pigments and a backing of felt or cellular PVC. The felt backing is of needle-loom felt and the sheets are 1.5 and 2.0 m wide. The foam backing is of plasticised polymeric material, stabilised and converted to a cellular state and the sheets are 1.2, 1.5, 1.8, 2.0 and 2.1 m wide and 2.0, 2.5, 3.0 and 4.5 mm thick. These flexible sheets are heat welded together to make a seamless floor. This floor is hardwearing and soft and quiet underfoot due to the backing and is much used in hospitals and public buildings for ease of cleaning and sound deadening effect.

Thermoplastic and PVC tiles and sheets should be laid on a carefully prepared smooth surface screed, as even small variations in the surface of the screed will show through these thin materials. The tiles and sheets are bonded with an adhesive that is spread evenly, by trowel, over the screed and the tiles and sheets are then pressed into place. These tiles and sheets should be warmed before laying in cold conditions. The flexible backed PVC sheets are laid on a carefully prepared screed and bonded to an adhesive that is spread evenly by trowel and the sheets are then rolled to make a good bond to the adhesive.

Plastic floor finishes do not dust, are easily cleaned and may be polished for appearance sake and ease of cleaning. They tend to be slippery when wet, wear moderately well and quickly show scuff marks and the indent of heavy furniture and scratches.

Linoleum is made from powdered cork, fillers and pigments and oxidised linseed oil with a backing and reinforcement of jute canvas supplied in sheet and tile form in widths of 1830 for sheets and 300 square tiles and thicknesses of 2.0, 2.5, 3.2 and 4.5 mm. This resilient, hard wearing, easy to clean floor finish is less used than it was, having been replaced largely by plastic sheets and tiles. It requires more skill in cutting and laying than plastic flooring. It does not dust, can be cleaned by washing and is fairly readily indented and scratched. With reasonable care it is an admirable, durable floor finish.

Wood and wood-based finishes

Wood floor finishes for concrete floors: Wood as a floor finish is prepared as either strip flooring or as wood blocks. Generally wood strip flooring, which is expensive, is used where wear on the surface is light, as in houses, and wood blocks for houses, public buildings, offices and schools.

Wood strip flooring: Strips of hardwood or softwood of good quality, specially selected so as to be particularly free of knots, are prepared in widths of 90 or less and 19, 21 or 28 in thickness. The type of wood chosen is one which is thought to have an attractive natural colour and decorative grain. The edges of the strip are cut so that one edge is grooved and the other edge tongued, so that when they are put together the tongue on one fits tightly into the groove in its neighbour as in Fig. 107. The strips are said to be tongued and grooved, usually abbreviated to T & G. The main purpose of the tongue and groove is to cause the strips to interlock so that any slight twisting of one strip is resisted by its neighbour.

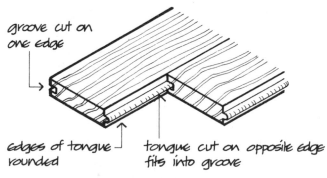

groove cut on one edge

edges of tongue rounded

tongue cut on opposite edge fits into groove

T. & G. strip flooring

Fig. 107

There is always some tendency for wood strips to twist out of flat, due to the wood drying out and to resist this the strips have to be securely nailed to wood battens which are secured to the concrete floor either by means of galvanised metal floor clips, or in a cement and sand screed. The drawing of part of a concrete floor finished with wood strips nailed to battens will explain the arrangement of the parts, Fig. 108. The floor clips are of galvanised sheet steel which is cut and stamped to the shape shown in Fig. 108. The floor clips are usually set into the concrete floor whilst it is still wet. They are placed in rows 450 apart and the clips in each row are spaced 750 apart so that, when the concrete has hardened, the clips are firmly bedded in it. The strip flooring is usually laid towards the end of building operations and the 50 × 38 or 50 × 25 softwood battens are wedged up until they are level and the clips are then nailed to them. The strip flooring is then nailed to the battens. An alternative method of securing the battens to the concrete sub-floor is to bed dovetailed battens in a sand and cement screed spread on the concrete as illustrated in Fig. 109.

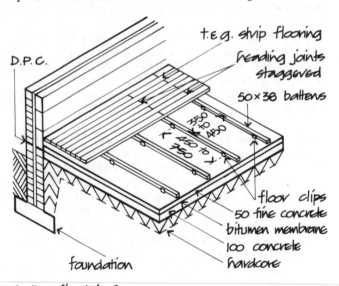

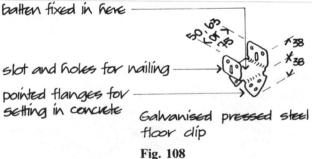

Fig. 108

If timber is in contact with a damp surface it will rot and it is important to protect both the battens and the strip flooring from damp which may rise from or through the concrete sub-floor. The battens should be impregnated with a preservative before they are fixed and either the surface of the concrete sub-floor should be covered with a coat of bitumen or a waterproof membrane should

be used in or under the concrete oversite. As wood strip flooring is an expensive, decorative, floor finish the strips of wood are nailed to the battens so that the heads of the nails do not show on the finished surface of the floor. This is termed secret nailings. If the strips have tongued and grooved edges the nails are driven obliquely through the tongues into the battens below so that the groove in the edge of the next board hides the nail.

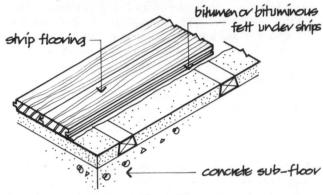

Fig. 109

Even though the nails used have small heads they may split the narrow tongue off the edge of the strip and this makes a poor fixing. To avoid this, the edges of the strips can be cut with splayed tongued and grooved joints. The finished surface of the wood strips is usually wax polished to protect it, show the grain and colour of the wood to its best advantage and to make it easy to clean the floor. Oak, beech, maple and birch are commonly used for strip flooring.

Wood block floor finish: Blocks of some wood with good resistance to wear are cut. The blocks are usually 229 to 305 long by 75 wide by from 21 to 40 thick. The blocks are laid on the floor in bonded, herringbone or basket weave pattern. The usual patterns are illustrated in Fig. 110.

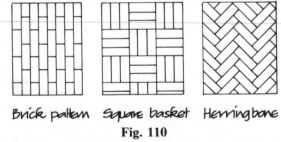

Fig. 110

Wood blocks are laid on a thoroughly dry, clean, level cement and sand screeded surface which has been finished with a wood float to leave its surface rough textured. A thin layer of bitumen is spread over the surface of the screed and into this the blocks are pressed. The lower edges of the blocks of wood are usually cut with a half dovetail incision so that when the blocks are pressed into the bitumen some bitumen squeezes up and fills these dovetail cuts and so assists in binding the blocks to the bitumen, as shown in Fig. 111.

If the wood blocks have been thoroughly seasoned (dried) and they are firmly pressed into the bitumen they will usually be securely fixed to the floor. It is possible, however, that one or more blocks may not be firmly fixed and will come up. To prevent this happening good quality wood blocks 25 thick and over have either tongues and grooves cut on their edges or wood dowels to joint them as shown in Fig. 111. When the blocks have been laid the surface is usually 'sanded'. The word 'sanded' describes the operation of running a power driven sanding machine over the surface. The machine has a drum surfaced with sand paper, which sand papers the surface until it is smooth. The surface is then either oiled or wax polished.

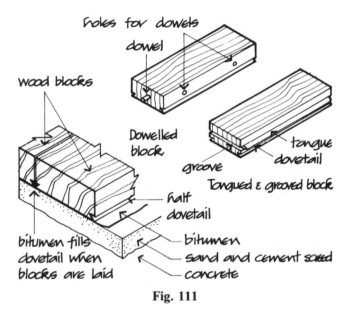

Fig. 111

Chipboard is the common name for particle boards that are made from particles of wood bonded with a synthetic resin, usually urea formaldehyde, and compressed into rigid boards 1.8, 2.1, 2.4, 2.7, 3.0, 4.6 and 5.3 m long, 0.6, 1.2, 2.5 and 1.7 m wide and 8, 9, 10, 12, 14, 18, 19, 22, 25, 31 and 40 thick.

These cheap, rigid, stable boards have a reasonably smooth surface, can be cut, nailed and fixed like wood and are much used as a floor finish or floor deck for applied finishes such as thin tiles, sheets and carpet. On timber floors chipboards 18 and 22 thick are used on joists at 400 and 600 centres with boards 2400 long by 1200 wide.

On concrete floors chipboards are fixed to battens in floor clips or battens nailed to the concrete base in the same way that boards are fixed. The advantage of the chipboard floor is that electrical, heating and water services can be accommodated between the battens and the boards. For use as a floor finish, chipboard can be sealed to prevent dusting, to facilitate cleaning and to avoid staining.

Thick tiled finishes

Tiled floor finishes: The word tile was first used to describe thin slabs of burned clay, usually rectangular in shape, which were used to cover roofs and floors. Similarly shaped slabs of other materials are today described as being tiles, for example, concrete tiles and rubber tiles.

Clay floor tiles: The two different types which are manufactured today are distinguished as floor quarries and clay floor tiles, The word quarry is derived from the French *carre*, meaning square. Clay floor quarries are thicker, less uniform in shape and size and have a less smooth surface than clay floor tiles.

Floor quarries are manufactured in Staffordshire and Wales from natural plastic clays. The clay is ground and mixed with water and then moulded in hand operated presses. The moulded clay tile is then burned in a kiln. If the clay is of good quality and the tile is burned at the correct temperature the finished tile will be very hard, dense and will wear extremely well. But as there is no precise examination of the clays used, nor accurate control of pressing or burning, the tiles produced vary considerably in quality, from very hard well-burned quarries, to soft underburned quarries unsuitable for any use in buildings. The manufacturers grade the tiles according to their hardness, shape and colour. The first or best quality of these clay floor quarries are so hard and dense that they will suffer the hardest wear on floors for centuries without noticeably wearing. Because they are made from plastic clay, which readily absorbs moisture, quarries shrink appreciably when burned and there is often a noticeable difference in the size of individual tiles in any batch. The usual colours are red, black, buff and heather brown and the tiles are manufactured in the following sizes:

Preferred modular co-ordinating sizes
    200 × 200 × 19
    100 × 100 × 19

Non-modular sizes
    229 × 229 × 32
    152 × 152 × 16
    152 × 152 × 19
    152 × 152 × 22
    150 × 150 × 15.

Clay floor tiles: Three types of these tiles are manufactured, plain colours, vitreous and encaustic.

Plain colours are manufactured from natural clays selected for their purity. The clay is ground to fine dry powder and a small amount of water is added. The damp powder is heavily pressed into tile shape and the moulded tiles are burned. Because finely ground clay is used the finished tiles are very uniform in quality and because little water is used in the moulding, very little shrinkage occurs during burning. The finished tiles are uniform in shape and size and have smooth faces. The tiles are manufactured in red, buff, black, chocolate and fawn and in the following sizes:

Preferred modular co-ordinating sizes
100 × 100 × 9.5 mm
200 × 100 × 9.5 mm

Non-modular sizes
152 × 152 × 12.5 mm
152 × 152 × 9.5 mm.

Vitreous floor tiles: The word vitreous means glass-like. These tiles are made from felspar which melts when the tile is burned and causes it to have a hard, smooth, glass-like surface which is impervious to water. By itself felspar would make the tile too brittle for use and it is mixed with both clay and flint. These materials are ground to a fine powder, a little water is added and the material is heavily pressed into tile shape and then burned.

The tiles are uniform in shape and size and have a very smooth semi-gloss surface which does not absorb water or other liquids. Colours and sizes are the same as those of plain colour tiles. Vitreous floor tiles are more expensive than plain colour floor tiles. These tiles are called tesselated by some manufacturers. The word tessellated derives from tesserae, meaning small pieces of tile. Other manufacturers call these tiles ceramic which means 'made from clay'. It is best to avoid the use of these misleading names.

Encaustic tiles: The word 'encaustic' is used to describe a tile which has a pattern, or design, inlaid in its surface in differently coloured clays. An ordinary plain colour tile is first press moulded with one or more shallow sinkings in its surface and into these sinkings are pressed one or more coloured clays. Clays of many different colours can be used to decorate the surface of the tiles. The tiles are burned in a kiln. The sizes of these tiles are the same as plain colour tiles.

Laying clay floor tiles: Clay floor tiles should be laid on a solid base of concrete. To accommodate relative movements between the concrete base, the screed and the tiles, it is good practice to bed the tiles over a separating layer, on a thick bed or on a thin bed adhesive. The relative movements that can occur are drying shrinkage of concrete and screed bases, differing thermal movements and creep of concrete. Where clay tiles are firmly bonded to the concrete or screed there is a likelihood of differential movement between the base and the tiles causing tiles to arch or ridge upwards so causing failure of the floor. Tiles should, therefore, be bedded in such a way as to accommodate possible movement.

Bedding on a separating layer: A separating layer of sheet material such as polythene or building paper is spread over the power floated concrete or screeded base with the sheets lapped to prevent any adhesion of the bedding to the base. The tiles are then bedded on a layer of cement and sand about 12 to 15 thick on which they are levelled and the joints grouted or filled, as illustrated in Fig. 112.

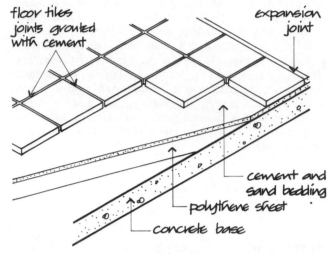

Fig. 112

Thick bed method: A bed of semi-dry cement and sand, mix 1:4, is spread over the concrete or screed base and packed to a thickness of about 35. The bed is then covered with a grout (wet mix) of cement and sand, mix 1:1, into which the tiles are bedded, levelled and the joints grouted or filled. The semi-dry bed accommodates relative movements between the base and the tiles.

Thin bed adhesive fixing: Tiles are bedded on a thin bed of a proprietary cement-based adhesive spread to a thickness of not more than 5. The adhesive provides a firm resilient base for the tiles that will accommodate movement.

Expansion joints: To take up possible expansion of tiles an expansion joint should be formed around the perimeter of a tiled floor as illustrated in Fig. 112. The joint is filled with an elastic sealing compound. For large areas of tiled floor, additional expansion joints should be formed both along and across the floor at intervals of not more than 7.5 metres.

Joints between tiles: The joint between tiles should be wide enough to allow for variations in the size of tiles and a joint of at least 3 for small tiles and up to 15 for larger tiles is necessary. The joint may be filled with a grout of cement or a mix of cement and fine sand.

Concrete tiles: These tiles are manufactured from clean sand and cement with a surface dressing of coloured cement and ground flint. The materials are mixed wet and heavily moulded into tile shape and allowed to dry out and harden slowly. The finished tiles are very hard and dense and are finished in a variety of colours. Sizes of tiles are 300 × 300 × 25, 225 × 225 × 19 and 150 × 150 × 16.

The tiles are laid on a bed of cement and sand over a separating layer of polythene or building paper on a concrete or screeded surface. The tiles are cheap, have a hard surface which wears well and can be easily cleaned.

RAISED TIMBER GROUND FLOORS

As explained previously many houses built in this country from about 1820 up to about 1939 were constructed with timber ground floors raised 300 or more above the site concrete or packed earth or brick rubble below. The purpose of raising the ground floor was to have the floor surface of the ground floor living rooms sufficiently above ground level to prevent them being cold and damp in winter. At that time imported softwood timber was cheap and this ground floor construction was both economical and satisfactory.

Since the end of the Second World War, 1945, imported softwood timber has been expensive and for some years after the war its use was restricted by government regulations. New buildings are usually constructed with raised timber ground floors only when the site is low lying and liable to be damp in winter. Most ground floors today are formed directly off the site concrete and this is finished with some attractive hard surface as described previously.

A raised timber ground floor is constructed as a timber platform of boards nailed across timber joists bearing on $\frac{1}{2}B$ brick walls raised directly off the site concrete. The following cut-away sectional view of part of such a floor will help to explain the construction (Fig. 113). The raised timber floor is formed inside the external walls and internal brickwork partitions, and is supported on brick sleeper walls.

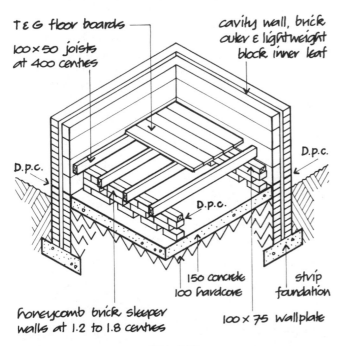

T & G floor boards
100 × 50 joists at 400 centres
cavity wall, brick outer & lightweight block inner leaf
D.p.c.
D.p.c.
D.p.c.
150 concrete
100 hardcore
strip foundation
honeycomb brick sleeper walls at 1.2 to 1.8 centres
100 × 75 wallplate

Fig. 113

Sleeper walls are $\frac{1}{2}B$ thick and are built directly off the site concrete up to 1.8 apart. These sleeper walls are generally built at least three courses of bricks high and sometimes as much as 600 high. The walls are built honeycombed to allow free circulation of air below the floor, the holes in the wall being $\frac{1}{2}B$ wide by 85 deep as shown in Fig. 113.

The Building Regulations 1976 require a space of at least 75 from the top of the concrete to the underside of a wall plate and at least 125 to the underside of the floor joists with adequate through ventilation of the space.

Damp-proof course

D.p.c.: A d.p.c. should be spread and bedded on top of the sleeper walls to prevent any moisture rising through the site concrete and sleeper walls to the timber floor. Any of the materials described in chapter 1 may be used for this purpose.

Wall plate: This is a continuous length of softwood timber which is bedded in mortar on the d.p.c. The wall plate is bedded so that its top surface is level along its length and it is also level with the top of wall plates on the other sleeper walls.

A wall plate is usually 100×75 timber and is laid on one 100 face so that there is 100 surface width on which the timber joists bear. The function of a wall plate for timber joists is two-fold. It forms a firm level surface on which the timber joists can bear and to which they can be nailed and it spreads the point load from joists uniformly along the length of the wall below.

Floor joists: These are rectangular section softwood timbers laid with their long sectional axis vertical and laid parallel spaced from 400 to 600 apart. Floor joists are from 38 to 50 thick and from 75 to 125 deep. The span of a joist is the distance measured along its length between walls that support it. The sleeper walls built to support the joists are usually 1.8 apart or less, and the span of the joists in this type of floor is therefore 1.8 or less.

Timber boards are laid across the joists and they are nailed to them to form a firm level floor surface.

From a calculation of the dead and imposed loads on the floor the most economical size and spacing of joists can be selected from the tables in Schedule 6 of The Building Regulations 1976 and from this the spacing of the sleeper walls to support the joists.

Similarly the thickness of the floor boards to be used will determine the spacing of the joists, the thicker the board the greater the spacing of the joists. Table 25 of Schedule 6 of The Building Regulations 1976 gives maximum spacing of joists for boards with a maximum of 505 for 16 board and 790 for 28 T & G boards.

Floor boards: Any length of timber 100 or more wide and under 50 thick is called a board. Floor boards for timber floors are usually 16, 19, 21 or 28 thick and from 100 to 180 wide and in length up to about 5.0. The boards are cut from whitewood which is moderately cheap or from redwood which is more expensive but which wears better. The edges of the boards may be cut square, or plain edged, which is the cheapest way of cutting them. But as the boards shrink ugly cracks may appear between them.

The most usual way of cutting the boards is with a projecting tongue on one edge and a groove on the opposite edge of each board, as in Fig. 107. The boards are then said to be tongued and grooved abbreviated to T & G. The boards are laid across the floor joists and cramped together. Cramping describes the operation of forcing the edges of the boards tightly together so that the tongues fit firmly into the grooves and there are no open cracks between the boards. The boards as they are cramped up are nailed to the joists with two nails to each board bearing on each joist.

Heading joints: Floors of small rooms can often be covered with boards sufficiently long to run in one length from wall to wall but in most rooms the ends of boards have to be cut to butt together. The joint between the end of one board and the end of another is described as the heading joint. The appearance of a boarded floor is spoiled if the heading joints run in a continuous line across the floor because the cut ends of the boards tend to be somewhat ragged and the continuous joint looks ragged and ugly (Fig. 114). The heading joints in floor boards should always be staggered in some regular manner. Obviously the heading joint ends of boards must be cut so that the ends of both boards rest on a joist to which the ends are nailed. A usual method of staggering heading joints is shown in Fig. 114.

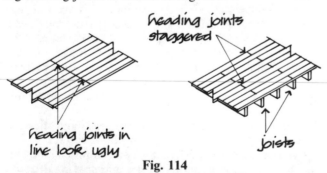

Fig. 114

End matched flooring: Some hardwood strips are prepared with tongues and grooves on the ends of the strips so that their ends firmly interlock and do not have to lie over a joist. The strips of flooring are said to be end matched. The end joint so formed is much neater than a sawn end of ordinary boarding.

End support of floor joists: The floor joists of the raised timber ground floor bear on wall plates on sleeper walls and the best method of supporting the ends of the joists at external walls and at internal brick partitions is to build a honeycombed sleeper wall some 50 away from the wall

to carry the ends of the joists, as shown in Fig. 115. The sleeper wall is built away from the main wall to allow air to circulate through the holes in the honeycomb of the sleeper wall. The ends of the joists are cut so that they are clear of the inside face of the wall by 50.

Ventilation of space below raised timber ground floor: The space below this type of floor should be ventilated by forming ventilation gratings in the external walls below the floor so that air from outside the building can circulate at all times under the floor. The usual practice is to build air bricks into the external wall. An air brick is a special brick made of terra cotta (meaning earth burned) with several square or round holes in it and its size is 215 × 65, 215 × 140 or 215 × 215 (Fig. 115). At least two of these bricks would be built into opposite or adjacent external walls for each floor. The bricks would be built in just above ground level and below the floor as in Fig. 115.

The purpose of the air bricks is to cause air to circulate under the floor and so avoid stagnant damp air which is likely to induce the dry rot fungus to grow. The disadvantage of ventilating the space below this type of floor is that in winter the floor is liable to be cold. It is usual, therefore, to fix an insulating board or quilt under the floor boards to minimise transfer of heat to the ventilated space below the floor.

Air bricks in cavity walls: It is common practice today to prevent cold air from outside entering the cavity of a cavity wall to avoid the inner skin becoming cold. When ventilating air bricks are built into a cavity wall some means must be devised of preventing cold air getting into the cavity through the air brick. One common method of doing this is to build a roofing slate sleeve around the air bricks and across the cavity or a short length of pipe as shown in Fig. 115. A duct is made out of four pieces of slate which are built into the wall around the air bricks. Providing mortar droppings do not accumulate on top of the slate sleeve the slate will not convey water from the outer to the inner skin of the wall.

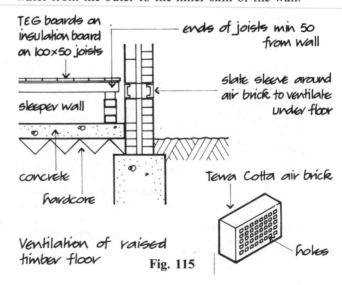

Fig. 115

70

UPPER FLOORS

Timber floors

As has been said a timber upper floor for houses and flats is about half the cost of a similar reinforced concrete floor. For upper floors of offices, factories and public buildings timber floors are not much used today because the resistance to fire of a timber floor, plastered on the underside, is not sufficient to comply with building regulations for all but small buildings. Concrete floors are used instead because of their better resistance to fire, and better resistance to sound transmission.

Floor joists: The floor is framed, or carcassed, with softwood timber joists which are usually 38 to 50 thick and 75 to 225 deep. The required depth of joists depends on the dead and imposed loads and the span. The spacing of the joists is usually from 400 to 600 measured from the centre of one joist to the next. Schedule 6 of The Building Regulations 1976 sets out the required size of timber joists for given spans and with given spacing of joists for various superimposed loads.

To economise in the use of timber the floor joists of upper floors usually span (are laid across) the least width of rooms from external walls to internal loadbearing partitions. The joists in each room span the least width. The maximum economical span for timber joists is between 3.6 and 4.0. For greater spans than 4.0 it is usually economic to reduce the span of the joists by the use of steel beams.

Strutting between joists: When timber is seasoned it shrinks, and timber such as floor joists, which is not cut on the radius of the circle of the log does not shrink uniformly. The shrinkage will tend to make the floor joists twist, or wind, and to prevent cracking of a plaster ceiling which this twisting would cause, timber strutting is used. The type most commonly used is that known as herringbone strutting. This consists of short lengths of 50 × 38 softwood timber nailed between the joists as in Fig. 116. The strutting is fixed between all the joists right across each room from wall to wall. Wedges and blocks of wood are fixed between the end joists and the wall as in Fig. 116, to tighten the system of strutting. Alternatively a system of solid strutting is sometimes used.

This consists of short lengths of timber of the same section as the joist which are nailed between the joists either in line or staggered, as in Fig. 116. This is not usually so effective a system of strutting as the herringbone system, because unless the short solid lengths are cut very accurately to fit to the sides of the joists they do not firmly strut between the joists.

As with herringbone strutting the end joists are blocked and wedged up to the surrounding walls.

Usually one set of struts is used for joists spanning up to 3.6, and two for joists spanning more than 3.6. A single set of struts is fixed across the floor at mid span.

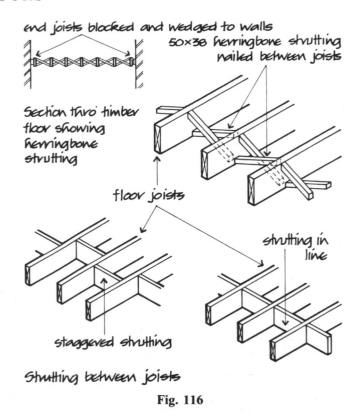

Fig. 116

End support for floor joists: For stability, the end of floor joists must have adequate support from walls or beams. If the floor is to be durable, timber joists should not be built into external walls where their ends may be persistently damp and suffer decay. Timber joists should not be built into or across separating or compartment walls where they may encourage spread of fire. Floor joists are, therefore, either built into internal and external walls or they are supported on hangers, or corbels projecting from the face of walls.

Timber floor joists that are built into walls should bear on a wall plate of timber or metal, which serves to spread the load from the floor along the length of the walls and as a level bed on which the joists bear.

Timber wall plates are of sawn softwood 100 × 65 to course into brickwork, and laid with one 100 face horizontal. The wall plate is bedded level in mortar to take the ends of the joists which are nailed in position to the timber plate and the wall is then raised between and above the floor as illustrated in Fig. 117, which illustrates joists built into an internal loadbearing brick wall.

When timber joists are built into the inner skin of a cavity wall the joists must not project into the cavity and it is wise to treat the ends of the joists with a preservative against the possibility of decay due to moisture penetration. The ends of joists built into a cavity wall may bear on a timber wall plate which should also be treated with a preservative. The wall plate is bedded on the blockwork inner skin. As an alternative, a mild steel bar 75 × 6 may be used. This metal wall plate is tarred and sanded and bedded level in mortar, and the joist ends bear on the plate as illustrated in Fig. 118.

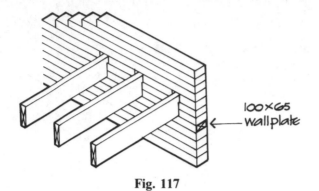

Fig. 117

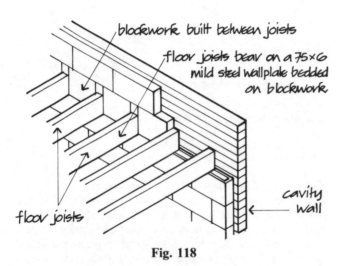

blockwork built between joists

floor joists bear on a 75×6 mild steel wallplate bedded on blockwork

floor joists

cavity wall

Fig. 118

Instead of using a timber or a metal wall plate the joists may bear directly on the brick or block wall with tile or slate slips in mortar packed under each joist end to level the joists. This is a somewhat laborious procedure and the slips may be displaced and the joists move out of level during subsequent building operations.

Timber joists may be built into a solid external wall if the wall is thick enough to prevent penetration of moisture to the joist ends and where the wall is protected externally with slate or tile hanging. As a precaution against the possibility of decay due to unforeseen moisture penetration it is wise to protect the joist ends and timber wall plates with a preservative.

Where timber floor joists are supported by solid external walls through which rain might penetrate to the ends of joists built into the wall, and where joists are supported by separating walls as in the cross wall form of construction, it is common to support the joists in galvanised pressed steel joist hangers made for the purpose. These hangers, illustrated in Fig. 119, are built into brick or block courses so that they project and support the ends of joists as illustrated in Fig. 119. Either the hangers are built in as the brick or block wall is raised

and the joists fitted later, or the joists, with the hangers nailed to their ends, are given temporary support as the brick or blockwork is built, and the hangers built into horizontal courses to accurately locate them in position. Metal hangers may be used to support joists on the inner skin of a cavity wall providing the span of the floor and the loads on the floor are not such as to be likely to cause so great an eccentric load likely to overturn the wall.

As an alternative to hangers, timber floor joists may be supported by a timber wall plate carried on iron corbels built into walls as illustrated in Fig. 120, or on brick courses corbelled out from the wall as illustrated in Fig. 120. The disadvantage of these two methods of support is that they form a projection below the ceiling. Since the advent of metal joist hangers, corbel bracket and corbel course support for joists have been little used.

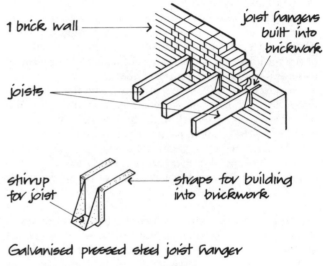

1 brick wall

joist hangers built into brickwork

joists

stirrup for joist

straps for building into brickwork

Galvanised pressed steel joist hanger

Fig. 119

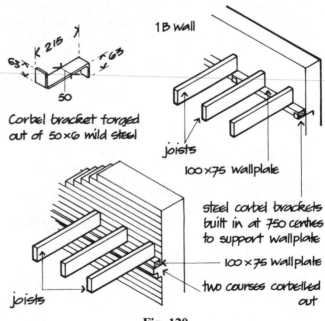

Corbel bracket forged out of 50×6 mild steel

1B wall

joists

100×75 wallplate

steel corbel brackets built in at 750 centres to support wallplate

100×75 wallplate

two courses corbelled out

joists

Fig. 120

Lateral support for walls: Where a timber floor gives lateral support to a wall to stiffen it, the timber joists have to be firmly anchored to the wall to give positive support. Metal ties are screwed or bolted to the ends of joists and the turned down end of the ties built into the wall as illustrated in Fig. 66. Where a timber floor gives lateral support to a wall parallel to the span of the joists then ties are secured across the joists and the ties anchored to the wall as illustrated in Fig. 66. Similarly, concrete floors giving lateral support are built in as illustrated in Fig. 66.

Sound insulation: A boarded timber floor with a plaster ceiling is a poor insulator against the transfer of sound. The sound insulation of a timber floor may be improved by the use of a sound deadening quilt, such as glass wool, draped over the joists and in addition some material between the joists as illustrated in Fig. 121. The quilt will deaden impact sound and to some extent airborne sound. The material fixed, poured or placed between the joists will insulate against transfer of airborne sound. The materials used are insulating boards, loose mineral fill or plaster, the more dense the material the greater the insulating value. The floor boards may be nailed to the joists through the quilt or nailed to separate battens fixed to the back of the boards that are then turned over and laid on the joists. Because there is no direct contact of boards to joist, impact sound is more effectively deadened.

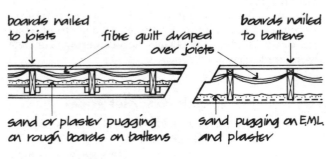

Sound insulation of timber floor

Fig. 121

Double floors: Where the span of a timber floor is greater than the commercially available length of timber and where, for example, joists span parallel to a cross wall it is convenient and economic to use a steel beam or timber beam to support timber joists. This combination of a beam and the joists is described as a double floor. Steel beams are generally used because of their smaller section. The supporting steel beam may be fixed under the joists or wholly or partly hidden in the depth of the floor. To provide a fixing for the ends of the joists, timber plates are bolted to the flange of the beam and the joists fixed to the plates as illustrated in Fig. 122.

Floor boards: The surface of the floor is formed by nailing boards across the floor joists. As with raised timber ground floors, the boards are usually 19 or 21 thick and have tongued and grooved edges. The boards are cramped up, and nailed and the heading joints of boards are staggered as described for raised timber ground floors.

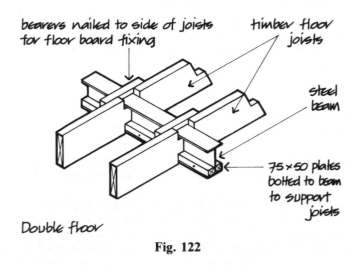

Double floor

Fig. 122

REINFORCED CONCRETE UPPER FLOORS

Reinforced concrete floors have a better resistance to damage by fire and can safely support greater superimposed loads than timber floors of similar depth. The resistance to fire, required by building regulations for most offices, large blocks of flats, factories and public buildings is greater than can be obtained with a timber upper floor so some form of reinforced concrete floor has to be used.

The following is a description of some of the concrete floors in use (see also Volume 4).

Monolithic reinforced concrete floors

The word monolithic means one stone and is used in building to describe one unbroken mass of any material. A monolithic reinforced concrete floor is one unbroken solid mass of between 100 and 300 thick, cast in-situ and reinforced with mild steel reinforcing bars. To support the concrete while it is still wet and plastic, and for seven days after it has been placed, temporary centering has to be used. This takes the form of rough timber boarding or steel sheets, supported on timber or steel beams and posts. The steel reinforcement is laid out on top of the centering and raised 15 above the centering by means of small blocks of fine concrete which are tied to the reinforcing bars with wire. The wet concrete is then placed and spread on the centering, and it is compacted and levelled off. It is usual to design the floor so that it can safely span the least width of rooms and two opposite sides of the concrete are built into walls and brick partitions $\frac{1}{2}B$ each end or where the floor gives lateral support to walls it may be built in parallel to its span.

Figure 123 illustrates a single monolithic concrete floor with part of the concrete taken away to show reinforcement and timber centering.

Centering: The temporary timber board or sheet steel support for monolithic concrete floor or roof is termed centering. The word centering was originally used for the timber formwork on which brick and stone arches and vaults were formed but today it is used to include the temporary support for concrete floors even though there is no curvature to the underside of the floor.

Reinforcement of concrete: A concrete floor has to carry loads just as a concrete lintel does and when loaded tends to bend in the same way. The steel reinforcing bars are cast into the underside of the floor with 15 of concrete cover below them to prevent the steel rusting and to give it some protection in case of fire. The thicker the concrete cover to reinforcement the greater the resistance of the floor to fire.

When the engineer designs a reinforced concrete floor he usually calculates the amount of steel reinforcement required for an imaginary strip of floor 300 wide spanning between walls, as though the floor were made up of 300 wide concrete beams placed side by side. The engineer will first calculate the combined superimposed and dead load that the floor has to support. The superimposed load is determined just as it is for timber floors and the dead load will include the actual weight of the concrete, the floor finish and the plaster on the soffit. From the loads and the span the required thickness of concrete will be determined and then the cross-sectional area of steel reinforcement for every 300 width of floor calculated. A rough method of determining the thickness of concrete

required for floors of houses and flats is to allow 15 thickness of concrete for every 300 of span. The main reinforcement consists usually of 12 diameter mild steel rods spaced from 150 to 225 apart, and these span across the floor between walls supporting the floor.

The 6 diameter mild steel rods wired across the main reinforcement are spaced at 450 to 900 apart and are called distribution rods or bars. These rods are tied to the main reinforcement with wire and keep the main reinforcing rods correctly spaced whilst the concrete is being placed and their main purpose is to assist in distributing point loads on the floor uniformly over the mass of the concrete.

In designing a reinforced concrete floor, as though it consisted of 300 wide beams, it is presumed that it bends in one direction only when loaded. In fact a monolithic concrete floor bends just as the skin of a drum does, when it is pressed in the middle. In presuming that the floor acts like a series of 300 wide beams the engineer can quite simply design it. But as no allowance is made for bending across the span, the floor as designed will be heavier and more expensive than it need be to safely carry its loads. The work involved in allowing for the bending that actually occurs in monolithic floors is considerably more than that required if it is presumed that the floor is a series of beams 300 wide.

Of recent years several firms have specialised in designing and constructing reinforced concrete and in order to be competitive their engineers make the more complicated calculation so as to economise in concrete and reinforcement.

Because the centering required to give temporary support to a monolithic concrete floor tends to obstruct and delay building operations 'self-centering' concrete floors are largely used today.

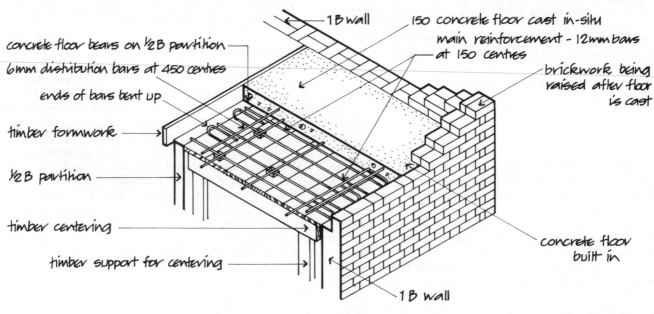

Fig. 123

Self-centering concrete floors

These are constructed with precast reinforced concrete beams which are cast in the manufacturer's yard and are delivered to the building site where they are hoisted to the level of the floor and placed in position. Once in position they require no support other than the bearing of their ends on walls or beams. There are two types of self-centering reinforced concrete floors: (a) hollow beam floor units, and (b) solid 'T' section beams and hollow concrete infilling blocks.

(a) Hollow beam floor units: Hollow reinforced concrete beams, rectangular in section are precast. Figure 124 is a view of part of one beam. The width of the beams is usually 355, the depth 130 to 205 and the length up to 5.5. The concrete walls of these beams are from 15 to 20 thick and the steel reinforcement is cast into the angles of the beams.

The depth of the beams varies with the superimposed loads and the span. These beams are not suitable for floors carrying very heavy loads such as the floors of warehouses.

The beams are placed side by side with their ends bearing $\frac{1}{2}B$ on or into brick loadbearing walls. If the ends of the beams are built into walls the ends should be solidly filled with concrete as the hollow beam is not strong enough to bear the weight of heavy brickwork.

The walls of the beams are made thin so that they are light in weight for transporting and hoisting into position. The thin walls of the beams are not strong enough to carry the direct weight of say furniture, and over them is spread a layer of concrete usually 50 thick which serves to spread point loads. The concrete is termed constructional concrete topping, and it is an integral part of this floor system. The concrete is mixed on the building site and is spread and levelled on top of the beams. In Fig. 124 is shown a view of a hollow beam floor. A hollow beam floor is lighter in weight than a similar monolithic concrete floor, but is deeper.

(b) Solid precast 'T' section beams with hollow lightweight concrete infilling blocks: Solid reinforced concrete beams generally shaped like an inverted 'T' in section are precast in the manufacturer's yard. Figure 125 is a view of part of a beam. The depth of the beams varies from 130 to 250 and they are 90 wide at the bottom. The beams are made in lengths up to 6.0. Hollow precast lightweight infilling blocks are made. These blocks are usually 225 wide and 225 or 300 long. They are made with one of the lightweight aggregates for lightness in handling and to reduce weight of the finished floor. The beams are placed at 270 centres with their ends bearing $\frac{1}{2}B$ on or into brick walls. The hollow blocks are then placed between the beams and the floor is finished with a 50 thick layer of constructional concrete topping. Figure 125 is a view of part of one of these floors.

The advantage of this floor over the hollow beam type is that its units can be handled by two men whereas hollow beams can only be hoisted by lifting gear.

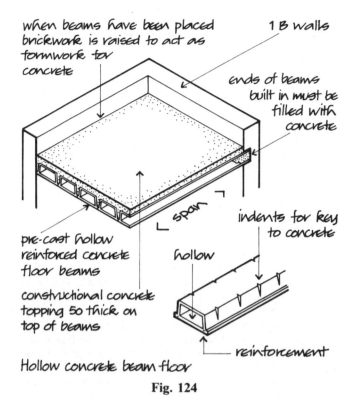

Hollow concrete beam floor

Fig. 124

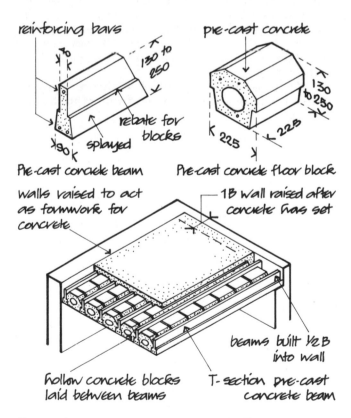

Pre-cast concrete beam and block floor

Fig. 125

Situ-cast reinforced concrete and terra cotta block floor
The resistance to damage by fire of a reinforced concrete floor depends on the protection, or cover, of concrete underneath the steel reinforcement. Under the action of heat concrete is liable to expand and come away from its reinforcement. If, instead of concrete, pieces of burned clay tile are cast into the floor beneath the reinforcing bars the floor has a better resistance to fire than it would have with a similar thickness of concrete.

The particular advantage of this type of floor is its good resistance to damage by fire, and it is sometimes termed 'fire-resisting reinforced concrete floor'.

To keep the dead weight of the floor as low as possible, compatible with strength, it is constructed of situ-cast reinforced concrete beams with hollow terra cotta infilling blocks cast in between the beams. The words terra cotta mean 'earth burned'. The words terra cotta are used in the building industry to describe selected plastic clays which contain in their natural state some vitrifying material. After burning, the clay has a smooth hard surface which does not readily absorb water. The blocks are made hollow so that they will be light in weight and the smooth faces of the blocks are indented with grooves, during moulding, to give a good 'key' for plaster and concrete. A typical T.C. (terra cotta) block is shown in Fig. 126. This type of floor has to be given temporary support with timber or steel centering. The T.C. blocks and the reinforcement are set out on the centering, and pieces (slips) of clay tile are placed underneath the reinforcing bars. Concrete is then placed and compacted between the T.C. blocks and spread 50 thick over the top of the blocks. Figure 126 is a view of part of one of these floors.

The floor is built into walls $\frac{1}{2}B$ as shown. This type of floor can span up to 5.0 and the depth of the blocks,

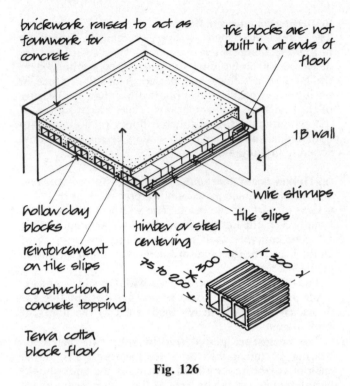

brickwork raised to act as formwork for concrete

the blocks are not built in at ends of floor

1B wall

wire stirrups

tile slips

hollow clay blocks

reinforcement on tile slips

timber or steel centering

constructional concrete topping

75 to 200   300   300

Terra cotta block floor

Fig. 126

the depth of the finished floor and the size and number of reinforcing bars depend on the superimposed loads and span.

Floor finishes to concrete upper floors: The various types of floor finishes described for solid concrete ground floors are used and applied in exactly the same way for upper concrete floors.

CHAPTER FOUR

ROOFS

The functional requirements of a roof are:

Stability
Strength
Exclusion of wind and rain
Durability
Fire resistance
Thermal properties.

Stability: A roof is constructed to support the dead load of the roof structure and its covering, insulation and internal finishes, snow loads and pressure or suction due to wind without undue deflection or distortion. The dead load can be calculated from the unit weight of materials set out in BS 648. Snow loads are assumed from average snow falls. The pressure of wind on a roof will depend on the exposure, height and shape of the roof and surrounding buildings. Wind blowing across a roof will tend to cause pressure on the windward and suction on the opposite side of the building. The actual pressure of wind on buildings is very difficult to predict with any certainty. In the tables of roof member sizes given in The Building Regulations a wind load is assumed for all but exposed positions.

A roof may be constructed as a flat roof, that is a timber, metal or concrete framed platform which is either horizontal or inclined up to ten degrees to the horizontal, or as a pitched roof with one or more slopes pitched at more than ten degrees to the horizontal as illustrated in Fig. 127.

A flat roof is constructed in the same way as a floor as either a timber or concrete platform. The stability of a flat roof depends on adequate support from walls or beams and sufficient depth or thickness of timber joists or concrete relative to spans, and assumed loads to avoid gross deflection under load. The flat roof type, termed a monopitch roof, may be constructed as a sloping platform with a sloping soffit or as a triangular frame as illustrated in Fig. 127, with the ceiling flat and the roof sloping. This roof acts structurally as a pitched roof, as its stability depends on the depth of the triangular frame at mid span.

A simple pitched roof has equal slopes rising, that is pitched, to a central ridge with horizontal ties at ceiling level as illustrated in Fig. 127. The stability of a pitched roof depends on the depth of the triangular framing at mid span and it is this depth that gives a pitched roof its stability so that it can be framed with comparatively small sections.

Strength: The strength of a roof depends on the characteristics of the materials from which it is constructed and the way in which they are put together in the form of a flat platform or some form of triangulated frame.

Exclusion of wind and rain: A roof excludes rain through the material with which it is covered, varying from the continuous impermeable layer of asphalt covering that can be laid horizontal to exclude rain, to the small units of clay tiles that are laid overlapping down slopes so that rain runs rapidly to the eaves. In general, the smaller the unit of roof covering, such as tile or slate, the greater must be the pitch or slope of the roof to exclude rain that runs down in the joints between the tiles or slates on to the back of another tile or slate lapped under and so on down the roof. Larger units such as asbestos cement sheets (see Volume 3) can be laid at pitches less than that required for tiles. Impermeable materials such as asphalt and bitumen that are laid without joints can be laid flat and sheet metals such as lead and copper that are joined with welts can be laid with a very shallow fall.

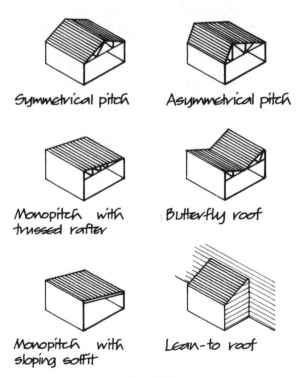

Symmetrical pitch   Asymmetrical pitch

Monopitch with trussed rafter   Butterfly roof

Monopitch with sloping soffit   Lean-to roof

Fig. 127

Durability: The durability of a roof depends largely on the ability of the roof covering to exclude rain. Persistent penetration of water into the roof structure may cause decay of timber, corrosion of steel or disintegration of concrete.

Fire resistance: A roof and its covering should have adequate resistance to damage by fire, and against spread of flame for escape in fire, for the periods of from $\frac{1}{2}$ to 6 hours set out in The Building Regulations.

Thermal properties: The materials of roof structures and roof coverings are generally poor insulators against transfer of heat and it is usually necessary to use some material which is a good insulator, such as lightweight boards, quilts or loose fill to provide insulation against excessive loss or gain of heat. The Building Regulations 1976 require high degrees of insulation in new buildings to conserve the increasingly expensive energy required to bring buildings up to the present-day standards of thermal comfort.

The most economical method of insulating a pitched roof is to lay or fix some insulating material between or across the ceiling joists, the area of which is less than that of the roof slope or slopes. This insulating layer will at once act to reduce loss of heat from the building to the roof space, and reduce gain of heat from the roof space to the building. As the roof space is not insulated against loss or gain of heat it is necessary to insulate water storage cisterns and pipes in the roof against possible damage by freezing. Where the space inside a pitched roof is used for storage or as part of the building it is necessary to insulate the roof slopes.

An advantage of insulating at ceiling level in a pitched roof is that there will be some ventilation of the roof space against stagnant moist air that might encourage decay of timbers. In warmer climates than the United Kingdom it is often practice to provide ventilation to the roof to reduce the temperature inside the roof.

Insulating materials may be applied to the underside or the top of flat roofs or between the joists of timber flat roofs. Rigid structural materials, such as wood wool slabs, that serve as roof deck and insulation are laid on top of the roof and non-structural materials either on the underside or on top of the roof below some form of decking. It is considered good practice to fix insulating material at or just above ceiling level in timber flat roofs so that there may be some ventilation between joists against moist air that might promote decay in timbers.

Vapour barrier: Insulating materials are effective against transfer of heat to the extent that they retain still air between fibres, in granules or in minute spaces. When these lightweight materials absorb water they lose their insulating properties as water enters the air spaces, and water is not a good insulator. Precautions must be taken, therefore, to prevent moisture or water saturating the insulation either through the roof covering or from humid air from inside the buildings. As a barrier to humid warm air from inside the building, an impermeable vapour barrier should be fixed between the warm air side and the insulation. This vapour barrier takes the form of a sheet of bitumen, polythene or aluminium that is impermeable to moisture.

FLAT ROOFS

Timber flat roof
The construction of a timber flat roof is just like the construction of a timber upper floor. Softwood timber joists 38 to 50 thick and from 75 to 225 deep are placed on edge from 400 to 600 apart with the ends of the joists built into or onto or against brick walls and partitions. As was mentioned with timber floors, Schedule 6 of The Building Regulations 1976 sets out the size of joist required for given spacings, loads and spans.

Strutting between joists: Solid or herringbone strutting should be fixed between the roof joists for the same reason and in like manner to that used for upper floors.

Roof boards: Boards which are left rough surfaced from the saw are usually employed to board timber flat roofs. This is called rough boarding and is usually 19 thick and cut with square, that is, plain edges. Plain edged rough boarding is the cheapest obtainable and is used for that reason. These square edged boards may shrink and twist out of level as they dry, and chipboard may be used in lieu of them to maintain a level roof deck. For good quality work tongued and grooved boards are often used.

End support of joists: If there is a parapet wall around the roof, the ends of the roof joists may be built into the inner skin of cavity walls or supported in metal hangers. The joists can bear on a timber or metal wall plate or be packed up on slate or tile slips as described for upper floors. The ends of the roof joists are sometimes carried on brick corbel courses, timber plate and corbel brackets or on hangers in precisely the same way that upper floor joists are supported. The ends of roof joists built into solid brick walls should be given some protection from dampness by treating them with a preservative.

Timber firring: Flat roofs are usually constructed so that the surface has a slight slope or fall towards rainwater outlets. This slope could be achieved by fixing the joists to a slight slope but the ceiling below the roof would then also be sloping. It is usual to provide a sloping surface to the roof by means of firring pieces. These consist of either tapered lengths of fir (softwood) nailed to the top of each joist or varying depth lengths of softwood nailed across the joists as shown in Fig. 128. Tapered firring is used for roofs covered with chipboard or wood wool slabs and the varying depth firring for boards laid parallel to the slope of the roof so that variations in the level of the boards do not impede the flow of rainwater down the shallow slope.

As an alternative to firring, some insulating boards are cut or made to a slight wedge section to provide the necessary fall to a roof.

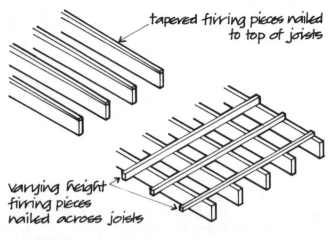

tapered firring pieces nailed to top of joists

varying height firring pieces nailed across joists

Firring to timber flat roof

Fig. 128

Thermal insulation: A timber flat roof provides poor insulation against loss or gain of heat. Most of the materials used in the construction of conventional buildings are poor insulators and some material has to be built into or onto the roof to improve its insulation against transfer of heat.

Any material that is to be a good thermal insulator must have a great number of tiny air spaces in it as it is the air trapped in these spaces that acts as the thermal insulator. It is common experience that fur and woollen garments conserve the heat of the body of the persons wearing them. These garments prevent loss of heat because of the air trapped by the many hairs or fibres of the garment.

Insulating materials are manufactured in the form of boards, slabs, quilts or loose fill and when used with timber roofs the boards and slabs are fixed on the joists under the boarding or on the underside of the joists. Quilted materials are usually laid between or over the joists and dry fill between the joists. The following is a description of the properties and uses of some of the insulating materials in common use.

Rigid boards are made from glass fibre, mineral fibre, polyurethane foam, expanded PVC or extruded polystyrene foam. The materials are supplied in lightweight, rigid board form in a variety of thicknesses from 12.5 mm to 150, lengths from 1200 to 3000 and widths from 75 to 1000. The boards may have a natural finish or be finished with a vapour barrier. These lightweight boards are used as insulation either on top of or below boards, as a ceiling finish or above the ceiling finish or fixed between joists.

Slabs of wood wool are manufactured in thicknesses of 25, 38, 51, 64 and 76 and 1800 to 4000 long by 600 wide. The slabs consist of coarse wood shavings bound together with cement and lightly compressed. This material is not so efficient an insulator as most insulating boards but has the advantage of reasonable mechanical strength so that the slabs can be nailed to the joists or firring pieces and the roof surface laid direct on them without the use of boarding. Slabs of 51 thickness are normally used and they appreciably improve the thermal insulation of a timber roof.

Quilts: Glass or mineral fibres are loosely packed between sheets of bituminous paper that act as a vapour barrier. These insulating quilts may be draped over the top of the timber joists, fixed above the ceiling finish or between the joists to provide good insulation.

Dry fill: Beads of expanded polystyrene or granules of a lightweight mineral are spread between the joists as a dry insulation, principally in existing roofs.

The density and thermal resistance of these materials are set out in table 8 on page 41.

Reinforced concrete roofs

All the types of reinforced concrete construction described for floors can equally well be used for roofs and the details of construction and advantages of each apply also to their use for flat roofs. The loads on roofs are usually somewhat less than those of floors and the thickness of a concrete roof will usually be less than that of a floor of similar span. The concrete of monolithic reinforced concrete roofs, and the constructional concrete topping of the other three types of concrete roof, is usually finished off level. If the surface is to be laid to a slight slope or fall the concrete roof will be finished with a screed of cement and sand, as described for concrete floors, with the top surface of the screed finished to the falls required. The least thickness of the screed will be from 20 to 25.

A reinforced concrete roof will usually span the least width between the external walls or external walls and internal loadbearing walls and will be supported on the walls and partitions in the same way as reinforced concrete floors.

Thermal insulation: A reinforced concrete roof provides poor insulation against loss or gain of heat, and some material which is a good thermal insulator should be incorporated in the construction of the roof or a lightweight concrete slab construction be used (see Volume 4). One way of doing this is to use a lightweight aggregate instead of sand for the screed. It will be remembered that a screed is spread over the concrete roof to provide a sloping surface for the roof covering. This screed can be made of lightweight aggregate in lieu of sand. The lightweight aggregates in common use are foamed slag, pumice and vermiculite. These three minerals are all porous and it is the air trapped in the minute pores of the materials which at once makes them light in weight and good thermal insulators.

Foamed slag is formed by spraying water on the molten slag which is poured off molten iron in blast-furnaces. The water causes the slag to expand into a porous light-weight mass. The slag is crushed into small particles. This is a moderately cheap material which is a good insulator. A screed 25 thick made of foamed slag and cement will appreciably improve the thermal insulation of a concrete roof.

Pumice is a rock of volcanic origin which is porous, light-weight and a good thermal insulator. It is crushed to small particles, mixed with cement and used as a screed. This is an expensive material not very much used.

Vermiculite is a micaceous mineral which consists of fine layers of material closely packed. When it is heated the fine layers open out and gases are trapped in the many spaces between the expanded layers. After heating it is described as expanded or more usually 'exfoliated' ver-miculite. The word exfoliated describes the opening out of the thin layers, or foliage, when the material is heated. This material is very light weight and is among the most efficient thermal insulators in use today. At present it is somewhat expensive. A screed made of vermiculite and cement greatly improves the insulation of a concrete flat roof.

Any one of the rigid, lightweight insulating boards may be used to improve the thermal insulation of a concrete roof fixed either on top or below the concrete roof. The most convenient place for the insulating boards is on top of the concrete roof, under the roof covering. By insulating the concrete roof from outside air, the concrete roof can act to store heat in continuously heated buildings.

FLAT ROOF COVERINGS

The materials used to cover flat roofs are built-up bitumen felt, mastic asphalt and the non-ferrous sheet metals, lead, copper, zinc and aluminium.

Built-up bitumen felt roofing

This is one of the cheapest and most commonly used roof coverings for flat and shallow roof slopes. The roof covering is built-up with two or three layers of bitumen roof felt, three layers being used for flat roofs and two for pitched roofs.

The three types of base material used for bitumen roof-ing are fibre, asbestos and glass fibre, the material of the base being felted and impregnated with bitumen. The surface of the underlayers is finished with fine mineral granules so that the bitumen does not bond in rolls and the exposed layers are finished with a mineral particle finish. The types and weights of felt are set out in table 10.

Glass fibre based felts have excellent dimensional stability, are non-absorbent and will not rot and are used

Table 10 Roofing Felt

Type of felt	Weight kg/10 m²
Underlayers	
Fine granule surfaced bitumen felt	18.0
Fine granule surfaced bitumen asbestos felt	18.0
Fine granule surfaced bitumen glass fibre felt	18.0
Venting base layer bitumen glass fibre felt	32.0
Exposed layers	
Fibre based mineral surfaced bitumen felt	38.0
Asbestos based mineral surfaced bitumen felt	38.0
Glass fibre based mineral surfaced bitumen felt	28.0

for good quality roofing work.

Asbestos based felts have good resistance to damage by fire, good dimensional stability and are used as a base layer for fire resistance and in good quality work for both underlayers and exposed layers.

The cheaper fibre based felts have low dimensional stability and are used for low cost roofing work.

On flat roofs bitumen felt roofing should be laid to a shallow fall of at least 1:80 to encourage run off of rainwater.

The method of application and fixing built-up bitumen felt roofing depends on the nature of the roof surface to which it is to be applied. The felt is laid across the roof with 50 side lap and 75 end lap between sheets.

Timber boarded roofs: On a timber board or chipboard roof surface with the insulation either under the boards or at or over the ceiling level, the first underlayer of felt is nailed to the boards either at 150 centres both across and along the roof, or at 50 centres along the laps of sheets and 150 centres elsewhere. The wider centre of nailing is considered adequate for fixing. The second underlayer is then bonded to the first in hot bitumen spread by mop or brush on the first underlayer, and the top, or exposed layer, likewise bonded to the second underlayer with the joints between sheets in each layer breaking joint.

The three layers of felt may all be of glass fibre base, all of asbestos base or an asbestos base first layer followed with two layers of fibre based felt. Figure 129 is an illustration of the roof and covering.

Dry insulation boards: Rigid preformed insulation boards may be used as insulation and the surface for bitumen felt roofing on a timber board or chipboard covered roof and on metal and timber roof decking (see Volume 3). Many of the rigid, dry insulation boards, except expanded polystyrene, are suitable for the direct application of bitumen felt roofing. The insulation boards are laid on an underlay of self-finished roofing felt, that serves as a vapour barrier against warm air from the rooms below. The underlayer of felt may be nailed, or partially or fully bonded on hot bitumen to the boards. The insulation

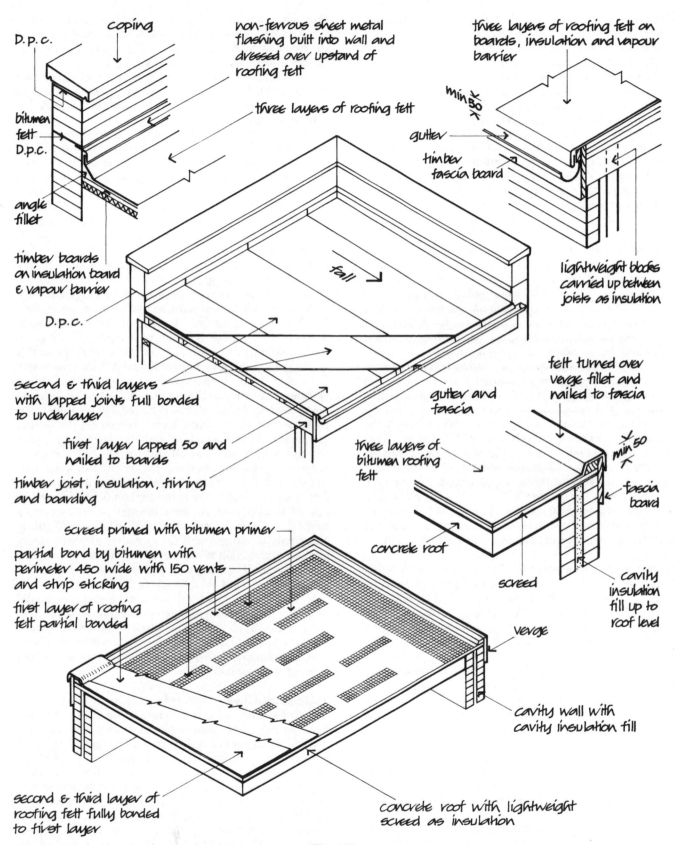

coping

D.p.c.

non-ferrous sheet metal flashing built into wall and dressed over upstand of roofing felt

three layers of roofing felt on boards, insulation and vapour barrier

three layers of roofing felt

min 50

gutter

bitumen felt D.p.c.

timber fascia board

angle fillet

timber boards on insulation board & vapour barrier

lightweight blocks carried up between joists as insulation

D.p.c.

fall

gutter and fascia

felt turned over verge fillet and nailed to fascia

second & third layers with lapped joints full bonded to underlayer

first layer lapped 50 and nailed to boards

timber joist, insulation, firring and boarding

three layers of bitumen roofing felt

min 50

fascia board

concrete roof

screed

cavity insulation fill up to roof level

screed primed with bitumen primer

partial bond by bitumen with perimeter 450 wide with 150 vents and strip sticking

first layer of roofing felt partial bonded

verge

cavity wall with cavity insulation fill

second & third layer of roofing felt fully bonded to first layer

concrete roof with lightweight screed as insulation

Fig. 129

81

board is then partially or fully bonded to the felt underlay, and the roof finish of three layers of glass fibre, asbestos or asbestos first layer and felt fibre layers is then fully bonded to the insulation boards.

Expanded polystyrene is not by itself a satisfactory surface for the direct application of bitumen felt roofing. The polystyrene boards must be heavy or extra heavy grade and prefelted. The polystyrene boards are laid on an underlay of roofing felt either nailed or bonded to the roof deck and the felted board of polystyrene is bonded to the underlay. An overlay of 13 fibreboard is then bonded to the polystyrene board as a surface for the bonding of the built-up bituminous felt roofing. These laborious procedures do not recommend polystyrene as the best insulating board material for the purpose.

Concrete screed finish: Cement screeds and particularly lightweight aggregate screeds on concrete roofs take time to thoroughly dry out and may absorb rainwater so that it is highly likely that some water will be trapped in the screed once bitumen felt covering has been applied. The heat of the sun will then cause this water to vaporise and the vapour pressure will cause the felt roofing to blister, crack and let in water. To relieve this water vapour pressure, it is practice to use a venting layer of felt on wet screeded roofs. This perforated layer of felt is laid dry on the screed and the three layers of felt are then bonded to it. Enough of the bitumen used to bond the first underlayer to the venting layer runs through the venting layer to bond it to the screed. The venting layer allows water vapour to be released through vapour pressure releases at abutments and verges of the roof.

Dry screeds, such as those on pre-screeded wood wool slabs provide a satisfactory surface for the direct application of bitumen felt roofing. The joints between the slabs should be taped with strips of roofing felt to contain the bitumen bond before the built-up roofing is laid.

Parapet walls and abutments: The bitumen felt roofing should be turned up 150 against parapet and abutting walls, over an angle fillet as illustrated in Fig. 129, and either the damp-proof course turned down over the upstand of the felt roofing or a separate flashing dressed over the upstand as illustrated in Fig. 129.

Eaves and verges: Either the bitumen felt roofing may be dressed over gutters with a welt or a separate non-ferrous drip may be used as illustrated in Fig. 129. Similarly, either the felt or a separate flashing may be used at verges as illustrated in Fig. 129.

Mastic asphalt

Asphalt (sometimes spelt asphalte) is defined as a mixture of naturally occurring material which is soft, has a low melting point and is an effective barrier to the penetration of water.

Natural rock asphalt is mined from beds of limestone which were saturated, or impregnated, with asphaltic bitumen thousands of years ago. The rock is chocolate brown in colour and is mined in several districts around the Alps and Europe. The rock is hard and because of the bitumen with which it is impregnated it does not as readily absorb water as ordinary limestone.

Natural lake asphalt is dredged principally from the bed of a dried up lake in Trinidad. It contains a high percentage of bitumen with some water and finely divided solid material.

Asphalt is manufactured either by crushing natural rock asphalt and mixing it with natural lake asphalt, or by crushing natural limestone and mixing it with bitumen whilst the two materials are sufficiently hot to run together. These materials are defined as *Mastic Asphalt for Roofing* (*Natural Rock Asphalt Aggregate*) BS 1162 and *Mastic Asphalt for Roofing* (*Limestone Aggregate*) BS 988. The heated asphalt mixture is run into moulds in which it solidifies as it cools.

The solid blocks of asphalt are heated on the building site and the hot plastic material is spread over the surface of the roof in two layers breaking joint to a finished thickness of 20. As it cools it hardens and forms a continuous, hard, waterproof surface. If the roof has parapet walls around it, or adjoins the wall of a higher building, an asphalt skirting or upstand, 150 high, is formed and this skirting is turned into horizontal brick joints purposely cut about 25 deep to take the turn-in of the asphalt skirting. It is essential that asphalt be laid on an isolating membrane underlay of black haired felt so that slight movements in the structure are not reflected in the asphalt membrane. A properly laid asphalt covering to a roof will not absorb water at all and the finished surface of the asphalt can be absolutely flat as any rainwater that lies on it will eventually evaporate. But it is usual to construct flat roofs so that the asphalt is laid to a slight fall, of at least 1:80, so the rainwater drains away to a rainwater outlet or gutter. Asphalt is a comparatively cheap roof covering and if the asphalt is of good quality and is properly laid it will have a useful life of some 20 years or more. The asphalt should be renewed about every 20 years if the roof is to be guaranteed watertight.

If there is no parapet wall around the roof it is usually designed to overhang the external walls, to give them some protection, and the asphalt drains to a gutter. Figure 130 illustrates simple flat roofs constructed with timber or concrete with and without parapet walls, and covered with asphalt.

Thermal insulation: To provide adequate thermal insulation to both timber and concrete roofs some insulating material has to be used. This generally takes the form of rigid lightweight boards fixed either under the roof covering or at ceiling level for timber roofs and under the roof covering on concrete roofs with a moisture vapour barrier between the insulation and the warm side of the roof as previously described. Where a lightweight aggregate screed is used it is practice to fix vapour pressure ventilation in the roof to release vapour from water trapped below the impermeable roof covering.

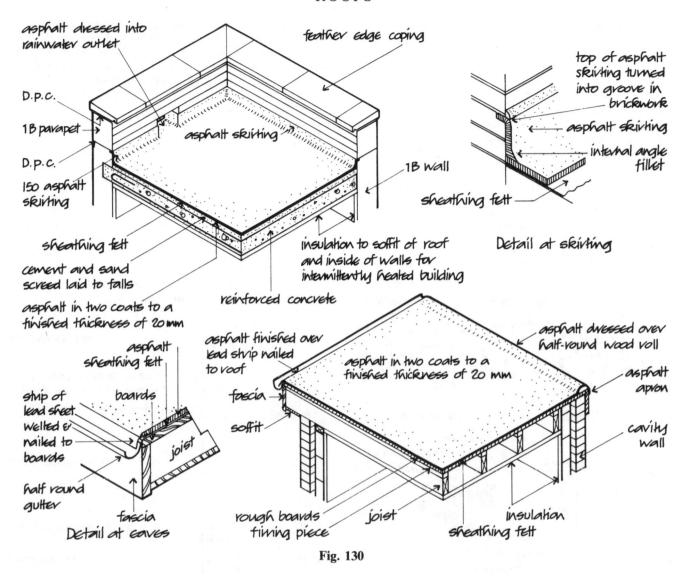

asphalt dressed into
rainwater outlet

feather edge coping

D.p.c.

1B parapet

D.p.c.

150 asphalt
skirting

asphalt skirting

1B wall

top of asphalt
skirting turned
into groove in
brickwork

asphalt skirting

internal angle
fillet

sheathing felt

Detail at skirting

sheathing felt

cement and sand
screed laid to falls

asphalt in two coats to a
finished thickness of 20 mm

insulation to soffit of roof
and inside of walls for
intermittently heated building

reinforced concrete

asphalt
sheathing felt

strip of
lead sheet
welted &
nailed to
boards

boards

joist

half round
gutter

fascia

Detail at eaves

asphalt finished over
lead strip nailed
to roof

fascia

soffit

rough boards
firring piece

asphalt in two coats to a
finished thickness of 20 mm

joist

insulation

sheathing felt

asphalt dressed over
half-round wood roll

asphalt
apron

cavity
wall

Fig. 130

Parapet walls: External walls of buildings are raised above the level of the roof as parapet walls for the sake of the appearance of the building as a whole. Parapet walls are exposed on all faces to driving rain, wind and frost and are much more liable to damage than external walls below eaves level.

Because parapet walls are freestanding, it is generally accepted that they should not be built above roof level higher than six times the least thickness of the parapet wall for the sake of stability. Solid parapet walls are usually 1B thick. The top surface of a parapet wall is exposed directly to rain and to prevent water saturating the wall it is essential that it should be covered or capped with some non-absorbent material. Natural stone was commonly used for this purpose as it is at once protective and decorative. The stones are described as coping stones and are cut so that they have a sloping top surface when laid and it is said that the stones are weathered. The stones usually project some 50 or more each side of the parapet

wall so that rainwater running from them drips clear of the face of the wall. The three most usual sections employed for coping stones are shown in Fig. 131.

From the above sections it will be seen that a groove is cut on the underside of each stone where it overhangs the parapet. The purpose of these grooves is to prevent rainwater running in along the underside of the stones to the face of the wall. When the water reaches the groove it is unable to travel any further and so drips off. For this reason the underside of the stone between the groove and the edge is called a drip. A detail of this is shown in Fig. 131.

Cast stone copings: Because natural stone is expensive, cast stone copings are commonly used today. Cast stone is made by specialist firms. The stones are made with a core of concrete faced with a mixture of crushed stone particles and cement. The surface of cast stone soon shows irregular unsightly staining.

D.p.c. beneath the coping stones: Coping stones are usually in lengths of 600 and the joints between them are filled with cement mortar. In time the mortar between the joints may crack and rainwater may penetrate and saturate the parapet wall below. If frost occurs the parapet wall may be damaged. To prevent the possibility of rainwater saturating the parapet through the cracks in coping stones it is common practice to build in a continuous d.p.c. of bituminous felt or copper or lead below the stones. This is illustrated in Fig. 131.

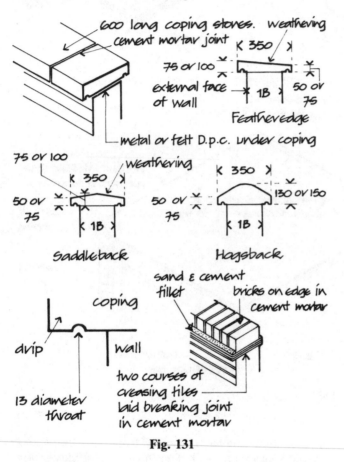

Fig. 131

Brick cappings: Another method of capping parapet walls is to form a brick on edge and tile creasing capping. This consists of a top course of bricks laid on edge, and two courses of clay creasing tiles laid breaking joint in cement mortar as shown in Fig. 131. The bricks of the capping are laid on edge, rather than on bed, because many facing bricks have sand faced stretcher and header faces. By laying the bricks on edge only the sanded faces show whereas if the bricks were laid on bed, the bed face which is not sanded would show. Also a brick on edge capping looks better than one laid on bed. Creasing tiles are made of burned clay and are usually 265 long by 165 wide and 10 thick. The tiles are laid in two courses breaking joint.

It will be seen that the tiles overhang the wall by 25 to throw water away from the parapet below. A weathered fillet of cement and sand is formed on top of the projecting tile edges to assist in throwing water away from the wall. Two courses of good creasing tiles are sufficient to prevent water soaking down into the wall and no d.p.c. is necessary under them. Parapet walls should always be built with sound, hard, well-burned bricks which are much less liable to frost than common bricks. The bricks should be laid in cement mortar, mix 1 cement to 3 of sand.

Parapet wall d.p.c.: It is good practice to build a continuous horizontal d.p.c. into brick parapet walls at the junction of the roof covering, upstand or skirting with the wall. Bitumen felt and asphalt covering a flat roof is turned up against the parapet as a skirting 150 high. It is at this level that a d.p.c. is usually built as shown in Fig. 132. This d.p.c. may be of bituminous felt, lead cored felt or copper or lead sheet. A metal d.p.c. may be continued as a weathering over the upstand of bitumen or asphalt as a flexible weathering to accommodate slight relative movements between roof and wall and in addition provide ventilation to timber flat roofs.

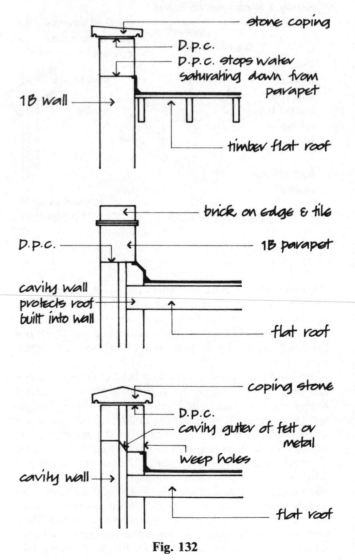

Fig. 132

Parapet to cavity wall: The construction of a parapet built on a cavity wall is usually somewhat different from that built on a solid wall. An external wall is built with a cavity to prevent rain penetrating the wall and it is logical to continue the cavity to at least the top of the roof, so that the cavity protects roof timber or concrete built into or against the wall. This construction is illustrated in Fig. 132. It will be seen that the cavity is continued to the level of the asphalt skirting. Above the d.p.c. the parapet is built in solid 1B work.

An alternative construction sometimes used is to continue the cavity wall up to the coping or capping as shown in Fig. 132. No good purpose is served in continuing the cavity walling up in the parapet as the cavity above the roof no longer acts as a barrier to penetration of moisture. The cavity is moreover an inconvenience in the parapet as moisture may penetrate the brick skins and water collecting in the cavity has to be drained out by the continuous cavity gutter shown.

Thermal insulation: To be effective the thermal insulation of a wall must be continuous for the height of the wall up to the insulation in the roof. Where cavity lining or fill is used in a cavity wall it must be carried up at least to the level of the roof insulation as illustrated in Fig. 133.

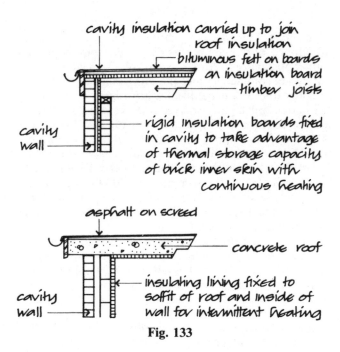

Fig. 133

Sheet metal roof coverings

Sheet metal is used as a covering because it gives excellent protection against wind and rain, it is durable and is lighter in weight than asphalt, tiles or slates. Four metals in sheet form are used, namely lead, copper, zinc and aluminium.

Expensive non-ferrous sheet metal roof coverings are much less used today than they were. It is not unlikely that recent steep increases in the price of petroleum products may bring them into greater use in the not too distant future.

The following is a description of the properties of these metals which can be used as either a flat or a pitched roof covering.

Lead: A heavy metal which is comparatively soft and has poor resistance to tearing and crushing and has to be used in comparatively thick sheets as a roof covering. It is malleable and can easily be bent and beaten into quite complicated shapes without damage to the sheets. Lead is resistant to all weathering agents including mild acids in rainwater in industrially polluted atmospheres. On exposure to the atmosphere a film of basic carbonate of lead oxide forms on the surface of the sheets. These films adhere strongly to the lead and as they are non-absorbent they prevent further corrosion of the lead below them. The useful life of sheet lead as a roof covering is upwards of a hundred years.

Copper: A heavy metal which has good mechanical strength and is malleable. Because of its mechanical strength this metal can be used in quite thin sheets as a roof covering. The sheets of copper can readily be beaten and bent to quite complicated shapes. Like lead, on exposure to atmosphere a thin coat of copper oxide forms on the surface of copper sheets which is tenacious, non-absorbent and prevents further oxidisation of the copper below it. Copper is resistant to all normal weathering agents and its useful life as a roof covering is as long as that of lead.

Zinc: One of the lighter metals which has good mechanical strength but is not so malleable as lead or copper. In sheet form zinc can be bent and shaped but it tends to become brittle and break. On exposure to atmosphere a film of zinc oxide forms on the surface of the zinc sheets. This coating is not as dense or adherent as that which forms on lead or copper and gradually the zinc below corrodes to form zinc oxide. For this reason the useful life of sheet zinc as a roof covering is only twenty to forty years for the thickness of sheet usually employed. Zinc sheet is liable to damage in very heavily polluted industrial atmospheres and should not be used there. The cost of zinc sheet as a roof covering is less than that of lead or copper sheet and it is often used for that reason.

Aluminium: One of the lightest metals. It has moderate mechanical strength and is as malleable as copper. It is resistant to all normal weathering agents. On exposure to atmosphere a film of aluminium oxide forms which is dense and tenacious and prevents further corrosion. Aluminium as a roof covering has a useful life intermediate between zinc and lead.

For many years sheet lead, copper and zinc were used to cover flat roofs but during the past thirty years bitumen and asphalt have replaced sheet metal as the principal covering for flat roofs because of their low initial cost. Of recent years sheet metal as a roof covering has come into its own again particularly for low pitched roofs. Architectural fashion has taken to the low pitched roof which is not sufficiently inclined for slates or tiles and hence the use of sheet metal coverings.

Size of sheets: The size of metal sheet used for roof covering is determined by the size of sheets manufactured and the need to allow contraction and expansion of the sheet. If too large a sheet were used and fixed to a roof it might well tear due to contraction. The following is a table of the size of sheet commonly manufactured:

Lead: Rolls 2.4 wide and up to 12.0 long
Copper: Sheets size 1.2×600 and 1.8×900
Zinc: Sheets size 2.4×900
Aluminium: Sheets size 1.8×600, 1.8×900 and 1.8×1.2.

Jointing sheets: As has been mentioned, the sheets of metal have to be fixed to the roof and jointed so that they can expand and contract without tearing and three types of joint have been developed which successfully joint the sheets, keep out water and allow the sheets to contract and expand without tearing.

All sheet metals are laid to a fall or slope on roofs so that water runs off. For flat roofs the slope is as little as 38 in 3.0, and the joints across the fall or slope of the roof have to be designed to allow rainwater to run over them whereas the joints along the fall can project above the surface of the sheets of metal. The joints along or longitudinal to the fall are usually in the form of a roll. Rounded timber battens some 50 square are nailed to the roof and the edges of the sheets are either overlapped or covered at these timber rolls. The joints across or transverse to the fall of the roof are always formed as a small step called a drip. The purpose of the drip is to accelerate the flow of rainwater running down the shallow slope of the roof. The following notes and illustrations describe the use of the four metals as sheet coverings to flat roofs.

Sheet lead: The usual thickness of lead used for roof work is 1.8 mm, 2.24 mm, 2.5 mm, 3.15 mm or 3.55 mm. These thicknesses are described as Code No. 4, 5, 6, 7 and 8 respectively, the Code number corresponding to Imperial weights of the sheet.

No sheet of lead should be larger than 1.6 m² so that the joints between the sheets are sufficiently closely spaced to allow the metal to contract without tearing away from its fixing. Another reason for limiting the size of sheet, which is peculiar to lead, is to prevent the sheet from creeping down the roof. The expression creep describes the tendency of the sheet to elongate. As the temperature of the metal rises the sheet expands but owing to its weight and poor mechanical strength it may not be able to fully contract as the temperature falls. The

consequence is that the sheet gradually elongates over many years and becomes thinner and may in time let in water. It is not likely that this will happen on a flat roof with a sheet not larger than 1.6². The joints across the fall of the roof are made in the form of a 50 drip or step down and to reduce excessive increases in the thickness of the roof due to these drips they are spaced up to 2.3 apart and the rolls (joint longitudinal to fall) up to 800 apart. The following is a view of part of a lead covered flat roof showing the general layout of the sheets and a parapet wall around two sides of the roof (Fig. 134).

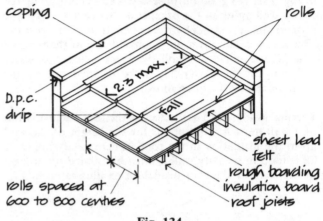

Fig. 134

Wood rolls. The edges of sheets longitudinal to the fall are lapped over a timber which is cut from lengths of timber 50 square to form a wood roll. Two edges of the batten are rounded so that the soft metal can be dressed over it without damage from sharp edges. Two sides of the batten are slightly splayed and the waist so formed allows the sheet to be clenched over the roll. Figure 135 is a view of a wood roll. An underlay of bitumen impregnated felt or stout waterproof building paper is first laid across the whole of the roof boarding and the wood rolls are then nailed to the roof at from 600 to 800 centres. The purpose of the underlay of felt or building paper is to provide a smooth surface on which the sheet lead can contract and expand.

The roof boarding on roofs to be covered with sheet lead may be fixed diagonally so that the joints between the boards are at 45° to the fall. It is wasteful of timber to lay boards diagonally as the end of each board has to be cut off at 45° and boards are, therefore, laid so that they run along the fall of the roof. The reason for laying the boards either diagonally or along the fall is so that if a board shrinks and warps it will not obstruct the flow of rain off the roof.

The edges of adjacent sheets are dressed over the wood roll in turn. In sheet metal work the word dressed is used to describe the shaping of the sheet. The edge of the sheet is first dressed over as underlap or undercloak and is nailed with copper nails to the side of the roll. The edge of the next sheet is then dressed over as overlap or overcloak. A section through one roll is shown in Fig. 135.

One edge of each sheet is dressed as underlap and nailed and the opposite edge is then dressed as overlap to the next roll. In this way no sheet is secured with nails on both sides, so that if it contracts it does not tear away from the nails.

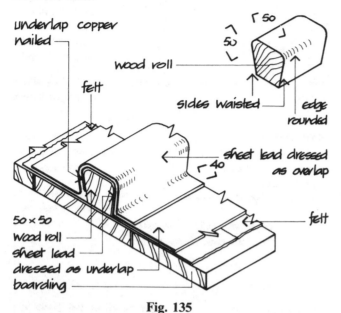

Fig. 135

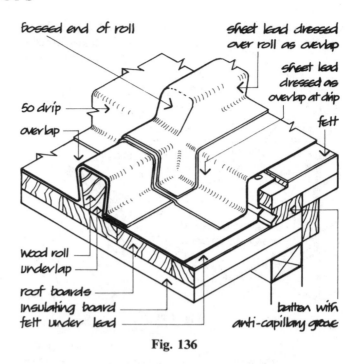

Fig. 136

Drips. Drips 50 deep are formed in the boarded roof by nailing a 50 × 25 fir batten between the roof boards of the higher and lower bays. The drips are spaced at not more than 2.3 apart down the fall of the roof. The edges of adjacent sheets are overlapped at the drip as underlap and overlap and the underlap edge is copper nailed to the boarding in a cross-grained rebate, as shown in Fig. 136. An anti-capillary groove formed in the 50 × 25 batten is shown into which the underlap is dressed. This groove is formed to ensure that no water rises between the sheets by capillary action.

Figure 136 also shows the junction of wood rolls with a drip and illustrates the way in which the edges of four sheets overlap. This arrangement is peculiar to sheet lead covering which is a soft, very ductile material that can be dressed as shown without damage. It will be seen that the end of the wood roll on the higher level is cut back on the splay (called a bossed end) to facilitate dressing the lead over it without damage.

Upstand and apron. Where there is a parapet wall around the roof or where the roof is built up against a wall the sheets of lead are turned up against the wall about 150 as an upstand. The tops of these upstands are not fixed in any way so that the sheets can expand without restraint. To cover the gap between the upstand and the wall strips of sheet lead are tucked into a horizontal brick joint, wedged in place and then dressed down over the upstand as an apron flashing. To prevent the apron from being blown up by the wind, lead clips are fixed as shown in Figs 137 and 138 which illustrate the junction of roll and drip with upstands.

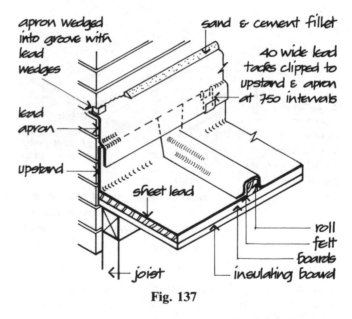

Fig. 137

Lead gutter. If the flat roof is surrounded on all sides by parapet walls it is necessary to collect the rainwater falling off at the lowest point of the roof. A shallow timber framed gutter is constructed and this gutter is lined with sheets of lead jointed at drips and with upstand and flashings similar to those on the roof itself. The gutter is constructed to slope or fall towards one or more rainwater outlets. The gutter is usually made 300 wide and is formed between one roof joist, spaced 300 from a wall, and the wall itself. Figure 139 shows the construction of the gutter.

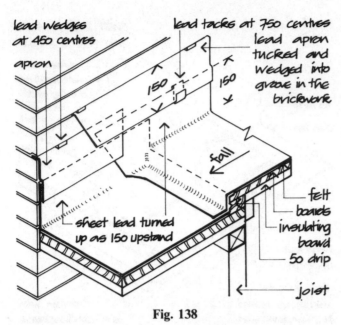

Fig. 138

lead wedges at 450 centres
apron
lead tacks at 750 centres
lead apron tucked and wedged into groove in the brickwork
150
150
fall
sheet lead turned up as 150 upstand
felt
boards
insulating board
50 drip
joist

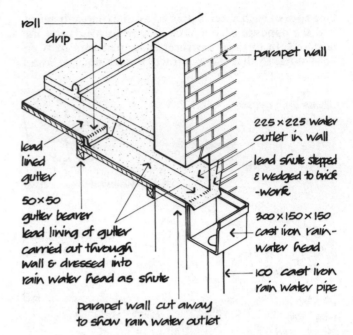

Fig. 140

roll
drip
parapet wall
lead lined gutter
50×50 gutter bearer
lead lining of gutter carried out through wall & dressed into rain water head as shute
225×225 water outlet in wall
lead shute stepped & wedged to brick-work
300×150×150 cast iron rain-water head
100 cast iron rain water pipe
parapet wall cut away to show rain water outlet

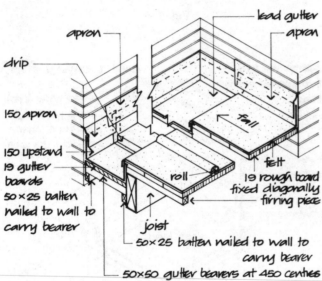

Fig. 139

apron
drip
150 apron
150 upstand
19 gutter boards
50×25 batten nailed to wall to carry bearer
lead gutter
apron
fall
roll
felt
19 rough board fixed diagonally firring piece
joist
50×25 batten nailed to wall to carry bearer
50×50 gutter bearers at 450 centres

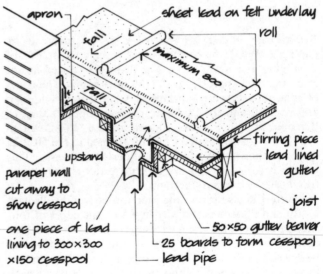

Fig. 141

apron
fall
fall
upstand
parapet wall cut away to show cesspool
one piece of lead lining to 300×300 ×150 cesspool
sheet lead on felt underlay
roll
maximum 800
firring piece
lead lined gutter
joist
50×50 gutter bearer
25 boards to form cesspool
lead pipe

Rainwater outlet. If the rainwater pipe or pipes can be fixed on the outside of the building, the gutter discharges its rainwater through a lead shute in an opening in the parapet wall to a rainwater head and pipe. This construction is illustrated in Fig. 140.

If the rainwater pipe can only run down inside the building, it is usual to form a cesspool or catchpit at the end of the gutter. The cesspool acts as a reservoir so that during a heavy storm, when the rainwater pipe may not be able to carry the water away quickly enough, the cesspool prevents flooding of the roof. The construction of the cesspool is shown in Fig. 141. If there is no parapet to one side of the lead covered flat roof it will drain to a gutter fixed to a facia board on the wall. This construction is shown in Fig. 142.

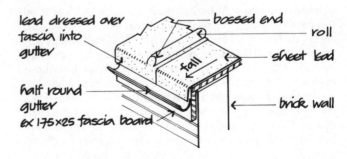

Fig. 142

lead dressed over fascia into gutter
half round gutter
6x 175×25 fascia board
bossed end
roll
sheet lead
brick wall

Copper sheet: The usual thickness of copper sheet for roofing is 0.6 mm. An oxide of copper forms on the surface of copper sheet and in the course of some few years the sheets become entirely covered with a light green compound of copper. This light green coating is described as a patina and is generally thought to give the copper sheets pleasing colour and texture. But in atmospheres heavily polluted with soot the patina is black instead of green. The patina, usually basic copper carbonate, is impervious to all normal weathering agents and protects the copper below it.

The standard sizes of sheet supplied for roofing are 1.2 × 200 and 1.8 × 900. The minimum fall for a copper covered roof is 38 in 3.0 and the fall is provided by means of firring pieces just as it is for lead covered roofs.

Rolls. The joints between sheets along (longitudinal to) the fall of the roof are formed over a wood roll fixed to the roof. Two sorts of joints are used (a) the batten roll and (b) the conical roll. Batten rolls are splay sided timber battens fixed to the roof at not more than 750 centres with brass screws, the heads of which are countersunk into the batten. The edges of the sheet are turned up each side of the batten and a separate strip of copper sheet is then welted to the roof sheets as a capping. A view of a batten roll is shown in Fig. 143.

It will be seen from Fig. 143 that the sheets are secured to the roof by means of copper cleats. These 50 wide strips of sheet are fixed under the rolls at not more than 450 apart and are folded in with the sheets and capping.

Instead of covering the wood roll with a separate capping the edges of the sheets can be folded together in the form of a double welt over a conical section roll. The rolls are fixed to the roof at not more than 750 centres. The arrangement of the copper sheets is shown in Fig. 144, and it will be seen that less sheet is required to form the conical roll than the batten roll joint.

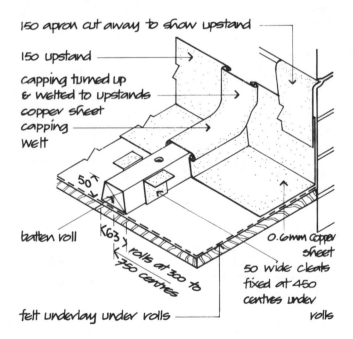

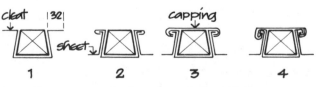

The four stages in forming Batten Roll

Fig. 143

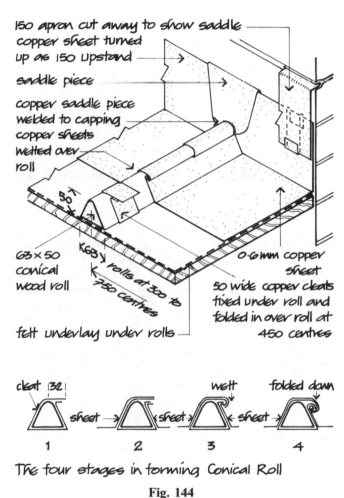

The four stages in forming Conical Roll

Fig. 144

Double lock cross welts. The drips formed in a roof covered with copper sheet are spaced up to 3.0 apart and their purpose is to accelerate the flow of water running down the fall of the roof. But as copper sheets are either 1.2 or 1.8 long some joint transverse to the fall has to be used between drips. This joint takes the form of a 'double lock welt' and because the joint is across the fall it is called a double lock cross welt. This joint is illustrated in Fig. 145.

It will be seen from Fig. 145 that the double lock cross welt is folded up with the sheets at rolls. To avoid too great a thickness of sheets the double lock cross welts are staggered as shown in Fig. 146 which illustrates a view of part of a copper covered flat roof.

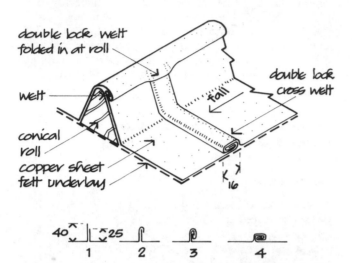

The four stages in forming a double lock welt

Fig. 145

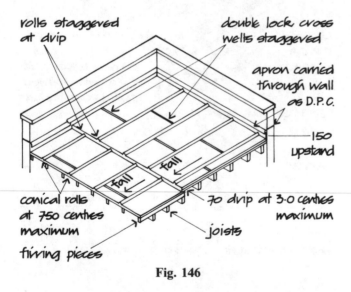

Fig. 146

Drips. These are formed at not more than 3.0 apart and a 63 or 70 step down is formed in the timber roof. The edges of the sheets are welted as shown in Fig. 147 which also illustrates the junction of the conical roll and a drip.

Upstand and apron. Where the roof is surrounded by a parapet wall or it adjoins a higher wall the copper sheet is turned up as an upstand average 150 high and this upstand is covered with an apron flashing as illustrated in the previous drawings of batten roll and conical roll.

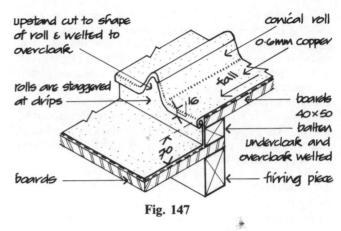

Fig. 147

Box gutter. Where the roof is surrounded by a parapet wall the rainwater is collected in a box gutter formed in the timber roof in exactly the same way as that formed for a lead covered roof. The gutter is usually 300 wide and drips at not more than 3.0 intervals are formed. The rainwater discharges either through the parapet wall to a rainwater head or to a cesspool as for lead covered flat roofs. The gutter is constructed as illustrated for lead lined gutters and the copper lining to it is jointed with drips.

Upstands and flashings are formed just as they are on the main part of the copper flat roof.

Eaves gutter. As copper sheet is thought to be an attractive roof covering the roof is not usually hidden behind a parapet wall and it is constructed to slope towards and discharge into an eaves gutter. Figure 148 is an illustration of the construction of the roof and the jointing of the sheets at such a gutter.

The arrangement of the batten roll end at eaves is identical to the batten roll end at a drip.

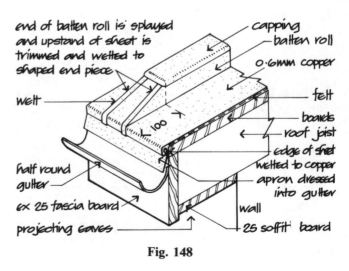

Fig. 148

Verge. Where there is no parapet wall around the roof the edges or verges of the roof down to the fall are usually finished with a roll and a flashing fixed to a fascia board with copper clips as shown in Fig. 149.

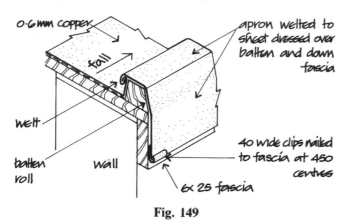

Fig. 149

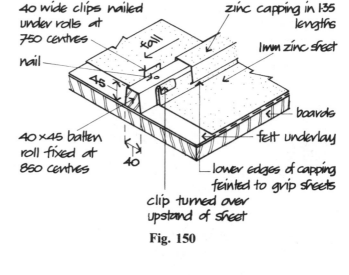

Fig. 150

Aluminium sheet: Aluminium sheet has a bright silver grey colour which in time gradually darkens. Pure aluminium containing at least 99% aluminium is used for sheet metal roof coverings. The sheets have moderate mechanical strength and can be readily bent and beaten into quite complicated shapes without damage. The sheets are usually 0.7 mm thick.

The usual size of sheet used is 1.8×600, 1.8×900 and 1.8×1.2. Sheets of larger size should not be used, as the lightweight metal, if not secured to the roof at fairly close centres, will lift due to wind suction and may cause disturbing 'wind drumming' vibration.

Jointing and fixing sheets. The thickness, strength and malleability of aluminium sheet is comparable to that of copper sheet and it is jointed and fixed to the roof in exactly the same way as copper sheet with either batten or conical roll joints along the fall and double lock cross welts and drips across the fall. The details of these joints illustrated for copper sheet apply equally well for aluminium sheet.

Zinc sheet: Zinc is a dull light grey metal which in sheet form has better mechanical strength than the other sheet metals used as roof coverings.

Zinc is the cheapest of the metals used as roof coverings and in Europe, where the metal can economically be produced it is very extensively used. In this country it has been much less used than lead or copper. Zinc sheet cannot so readily be bent or shaped as the other metals and the joints between sheets are designed to avoid much folding of the stiff metal.

The thickness of zinc sheet is 1 or 0.8 mm.

Jointing and fixing sheets. The standard sheet is 2.4 by 900. The joints along the fall of the roof are formed over a wood batten. The sheets are bent up on either side of the batten which is covered with a zinc capping as shown in Fig. 150.

The sheets are secured by means of sheet zinc clips 40 wide which are nailed under the battens at 750 centres and are turned up and clipped over the edge of the sheets as shown in Fig. 150. The zinc capping is secured by means of a holding down clip which is folded out of a strip of a zinc sheet. The zinc capping is made in 1.35 lengths. A length of capping is placed on the batten and the holding down clip is then nailed to the batten over the end of the capping as shown in Fig. 151.

The end of the next length of capping is inserted into the fold in the holding down clip and then placed on the batten and in turn secured with a holding down clip.

Using a standard 900 wide sheet the battens are fixed at 850 centre to centre. Using the standard 2.4 long sheet, drips are formed at 2.3 intervals down the fall of the roof and the following is an illustration of the two drip joints commonly used, and details of the junction of the rolls and drip, Fig. 152.

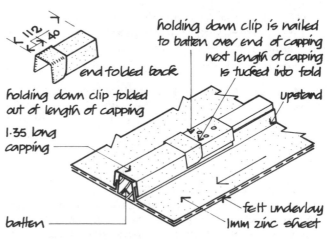

Fig. 151

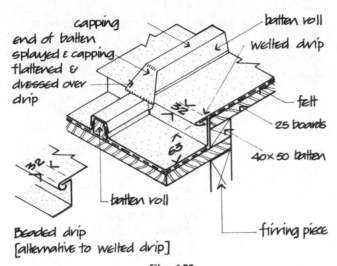

Fig. 152

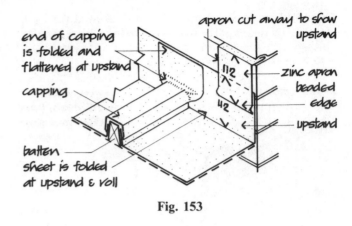

Fig. 153

Where there is a parapet wall around the roof the sheets are turned up against it 150 as an upstand and the upstand is covered with an apron flashing tucked into a joint in the brickwork as shown in Fig. 153.

If the roof is surrounded by a parapet wall it drains to a zinc lined box gutter similar to that used with other sheet metal roof coverings, only lined with zinc sheet. If there is no parapet wall the sheets drain directly on to an eaves gutter as shown in Fig. 154.

Sheet metal covering to concrete roofs: Because they are cheaper in first cost and easy to lay, bitumen felt and asphalt have principally been used as a covering to concrete flat roofs. But felt and asphalt only have a useful life of some twenty years and one of the sheet metals is sometimes used instead. The sheet metal is jointed and fixed to a concrete roof in the same way as on a timber roof. The wood rolls are secured to the concrete by screwing them to splayed timber battens set into the screed on the concrete or by securing them with bolts set in sand and cement in holes punched in the screed as shown in Fig. 155.

Drips should be formed in the surfaces of the roof just as they are in the surface of a timber roof and the details of jointing and dressing of the sheets is the same as those illustrated for timber roofs.

Roofing felt: It is essential that sheet metal be laid on a continuous layer of roofing felt laid on the surface of the concrete roof. The felt enables the metal to contract and expand freely and prevents it tearing on any sharp projections in the surface of the concrete roof.

Thermal insulation: Timber and concrete roofs are insulated against loss or gain of heat as previously described for bitumen and asphalt roof coverings. Where an insulation board or slab is fixed under one of the sheet metal coverings it must provide adequate fixing for the rolls or clips used to secure the sheeting to the roof.

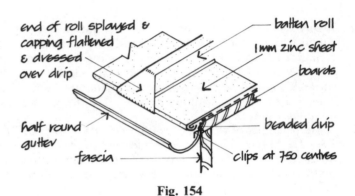

Fig. 154

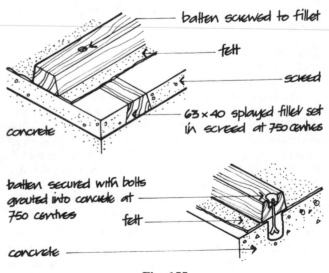

Fig. 155

PITCHED ROOFS

A pitched roof has one or more roof slopes at a pitch or slope of more than 10° to the horizontal. The most common roof shape is the symmetrical pitch roof pitched to a central ridge with equal slopes as illustrated in Fig. 127. A monopitch roof has one slope as illustrated in Fig. 127, which is a free standing version of the lean-to roof. Variants of these two simple shapes are the asymmetrical pitch and the butterfly roof as illustrated in Fig. 127. Figure 156 illustrates the terms used to describe the parts of a pitched roof.

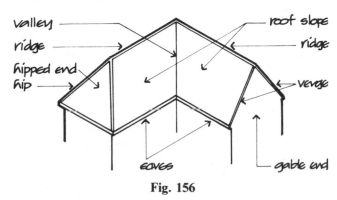

Fig. 156

The traditional English roofing materials, slate and tile can only successfully be used if fixed on to a surface inclined at least 25° to horizontal. The traditional way of constructing a roof with sloping surfaces is to pitch timber rafters either side of a central horizontal ridge, as illustrated in Fig. 157 with the rafters bearing on a wall plate on the supporting walls as illustrated in Fig. 158. This, the simplest form of pitched roof, Fig. 159, is termed a couple roof because each pair of rafters acts like two arms pinned at the top and the mechanical term for such an arrangement is a couple. The weight of the roof tends to spread the rafters of a couple roof and overturn the supporting walls, as illustrated in Fig. 160, and the span, or horizontal distance between wall plates, is limited to 3.5.

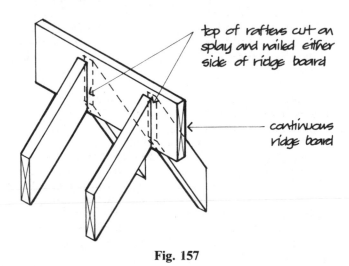

Fig. 157

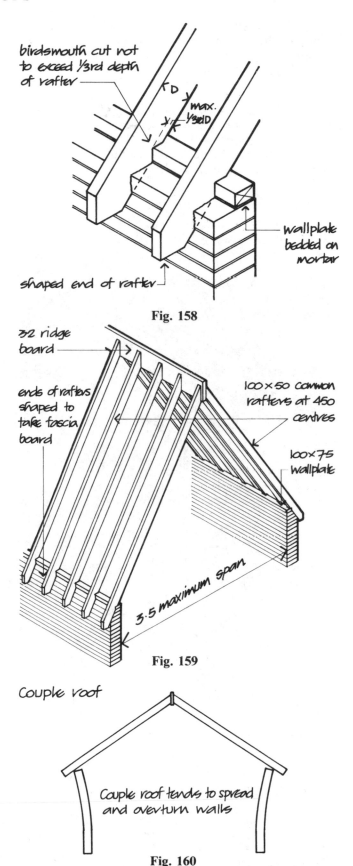

Fig. 158

Fig. 159

Couple roof

Fig. 160

In the traditional pitched roof form, timber ties are nailed to the foot of pairs of rafters to prevent them spreading under the load of the roof. These ties may also serve to support the ceiling finish. This type of roof, illustrated in Fig. 161, is termed a close (or closed) couple roof.

A modification of the close couple roof is the collar roof, where the ties are fixed between pairs of rafters, one third the height of the roof up from the wall plate, as illustrated in Fig. 162, so that rooms may extend up into part of the roof.

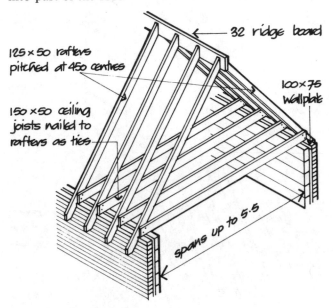

125 × 50 rafters pitched at 450 centres

150 × 50 ceiling joists nailed to rafters as ties

32 ridge board

100 × 75 wallplate

spans up to 5·5

Close couple roof   Fig. 161

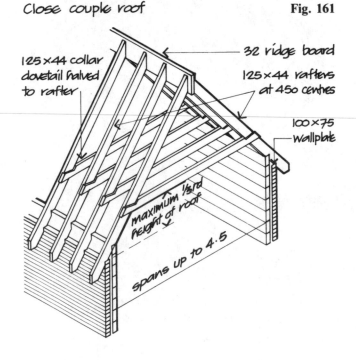

125 × 44 collar dovetail halved to rafter

32 ridge board

125 × 44 rafters at 450 centres

100 × 75 wallplate

maximum 1/3rd height of roof

spans up to 4·5

Collar roof   Fig. 162

With stress grading of timber (see page 55) allowing more accurate sizing of structural timber, the use of connector plates and factory prefabrications, the majority of timber-framed pitched roofs today are constructed as trussed rafters. A trussed rafter is a triangular roof frame of rafters, ceiling joist and internal webs joined with spiked connector plates and assembled in a factory. Figure 163 is an illustration of typical trussed rafter types. It will be seen that the trussed rafters are used in place of pairs of rafters and ties. A trussed rafter uses up to 60% less timber than a comparable traditional pitched roof and requires less on-site labour.

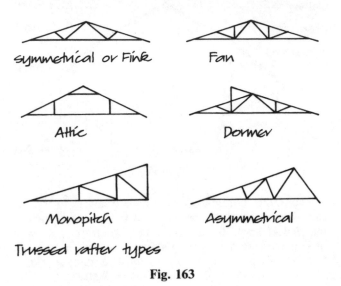

symmetrical or Fink   Fan

Attic   Dormer

Monopitch   Asymmetrical

Trussed rafter types

Fig. 163

Traditional pitched roof construction

Size of roof timbers: Rafters are usually 38 to 50 thick, 100 to 150 deep and are spaced at from 400 to 600 apart measured from the centre of one rafter to the centre of the next. The depth of rafters and the centres at which they are fixed depends on the type and weight of the roof covering they have to support and their unsupported length. In addition to the dead weight of the roof covering, such as tiles or slates, the rafters have to be able to resist the pressure of wind. The superimposed loads which roofs must be able to support are given in kilonewtons per square metre (kN/m²) of surface area of roof and are calculated to allow for the maximum pressure a roof is likely to have to withstand due to wind and the weight of snow on the roof.

Schedule 6 of The Building Regulations 1976 sets out safe sizes and spacing related to loads.

Ceiling joists (ties) are 38 to 50 thick and from 75 to 225 deep and since they are nailed to the sides of the rafters they will be spaced at the same centres as the rafters. Collars are usually 44 thick and are usually as deep as roof rafters. The ridge board is usually 25 to 38 thick and so deep that the whole depth of the splay cut ends of rafters bear on it. The depth of the ridge board will depend on the depth of the rafters and the angle at which they are pitched. The wall plate is usually 100 wide and either 75 or 50 deep and is bedded true level in mortar on the brickwork.

Eaves is a general term used to describe the lowest courses of the slates or tiles and the timber supporting them. The eaves of most pitched roofs are made to project some 150 to 300 beyond the external face of walls. In this way the roof gives some protection to the walls, and enhances the appearance of a building. The eaves of the roof of sheds, outhouses and other outbuildings are sometimes finished flush with the face of the external wall of the building. The purpose of this is to economise in timber roof covering. The construction of a flush eaves is illustrated in Fig. 164. It will be seen that the ends of the rafters are cut so that they are flush with the wall face and a timber gutter (or fascia) board is then nailed to them. The roof covering drains to an eaves gutter fixed to the fascia board. A building with flush eaves and pitched roof looks unfinished as though it were wearing a cap too tight for it.

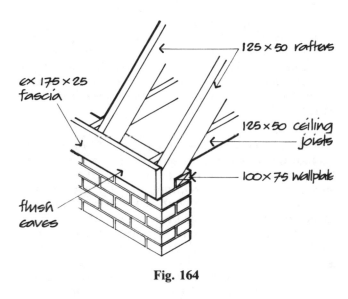

Fig. 164

Projecting eaves are constructed by making the ends of the roof rafters project as illustrated in Fig. 165. It will be seen that the ends of the rafters are cut so that a gutter board can be nailed to them.

Figure 165 is an illustration of an open eaves roof, so called because the underside of the rafters is exposed. To prevent wind blowing up into the roof between the rafters, beam filling is formed between them. This beam filling consists of brickwork raised between the rafters up to the underside of the roof covering.

Usually the soffit of projecting eaves is closed by fixing boards or sheets on it and this construction is illustrated in Fig. 166. It will be seen that short lengths of small section sawn timber are nailed to the side of each rafter

to form a bracket to which the boarding of the soffit can be securely fixed. Timber boarding 16 or 19 thick is usually employed for the soffit or alternatively strips of flat asbestos cement sheet are used. It will be seen from Fig. 166 that the wall plate is bedded on the external leaf of the wall so that the level of the soffit of the eaves is higher than it would be were the plate bedded on the inner leaf, so that the head of windows may be close to ceiling level.

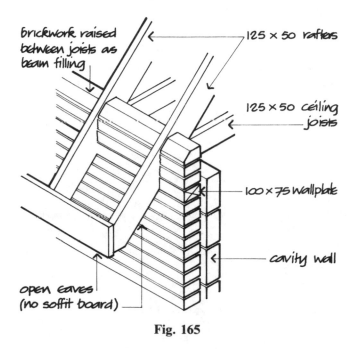

Fig. 165

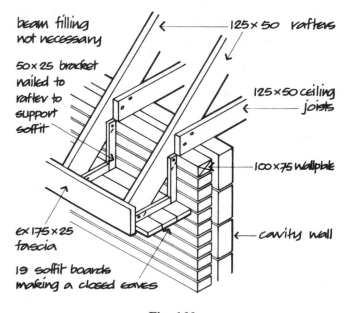

Fig. 166

Precast concrete eaves gutter: After the Second World War timber was rationed and in order to economise in the use of it a precast concrete eaves gutter was developed. The gutter is cast in 225 wide sections one of which is illustrated in Fig. 167. These gutter sections are bedded in mortar on top of the external walls and serve to carry the ends of the rafters and ceiling joists and also as a gutter to take the discharge of rainwater. Figure 168 illustrates the gutter position. The joints between the lengths of gutter section are filled with mortar and the gutter bed is then lined with hessian and painted with bitumen mastic to make it watertight. One of the advantages of this gutter is that it can be used as the lintel over the heads of window openings. A temporary timber support is formed at the head of the opening on which the sections are laid. Reinforcing bars are placed in the recess at the back of the gutter and concrete is poured into it. This makes a very effective reinforced concrete lintel.

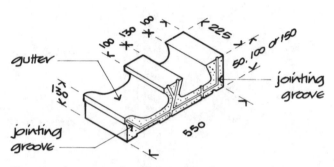

Pre-cast concrete gutter block

Fig. 167

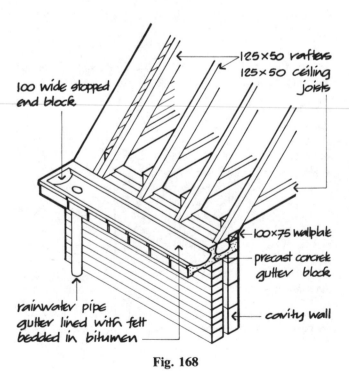

Fig. 168

Trussed rafter roof: The most economical size of roof rafters is 125 × 50 but a closed couple or collar roof with this size of rafter can at most only span 4.5 which is less than the width of most buildings. Timber-framed pitched roofs are usually constructed with trussed rafters, illustrated in Fig. 163, as this is the most economical and convenient way of framing pitched roofs today.

Trussed rafters are fabricated from stress graded timbers, accurately cut to shape and assembled and joined with steel connector plates. Much of the preparation and fabrication of these trussed rafters is mechanised, resulting in accurately cut and finished trusses that are delivered to site ready to be lifted and fixed as a roof frame. The connector plates are made from carbon steel which is stamped out so that the teeth protrude as illustrated in Fig. 169. The trussed rafter is assembled and the connector plates are machine pressed across the junction of abutting timber members of the frame to form a strong rigid joint.

A typical trussed rafter is illustrated in Fig. 169, consisting of rafters, ceiling joists and internal webs.

The trussed rafters are erected and nailed to a timber wall plate, bedded on the external walls, at centres to suit the roof covering. As the rafters are trussed there is no need for a ridge board or intermediate support between supporting walls. The eaves of the roof may be finished with a flush eaves or an open or boarded projecting eaves in the traditional pitched roof construction.

Purlin or double roof: Another way of constructing pitched roofs with spans of from 4.5 to 7.5 was to form a purlin roof. A purlin is a continuous timber fixed horizontally under the roof rafters to give them support between the ridge and the wall plate. The purlin in turn is supported by means of timber struts which bear on to a loadbearing partition. The arrangement of these timbers is shown in Fig. 170. It will be seen that purlins support the rafters mid-way between the ridge and eaves and that they are supported by struts at intervals of about 1.8 along their length. Collars fixed every fourth rafter serve to brace the roof and provide a secure fixing for the purlins which bear on them. The size of the purlins depends on the weight of the roof and their unsupported length between struts. With struts not more than 1.8 apart a 125 deep by 50 thick purlin is used for most rafters. Tables of safe sizes of purlin for various spans are included in Schedule 6 of The Building Regulations.

Collars of the same section as the roof rafters are fixed to every third or fourth rafter. Struts are usually 75 square in section. The foot of the struts is fixed to a timber wall plate bedded in mortar on the loadbearing partition.

The loadbearing partition does not have to be central between the external walls in order to give satisfactory support to the struts which in turn support purlins. If there are loadbearing partitions running at right angles to the ridge roof they can be used to support struts.

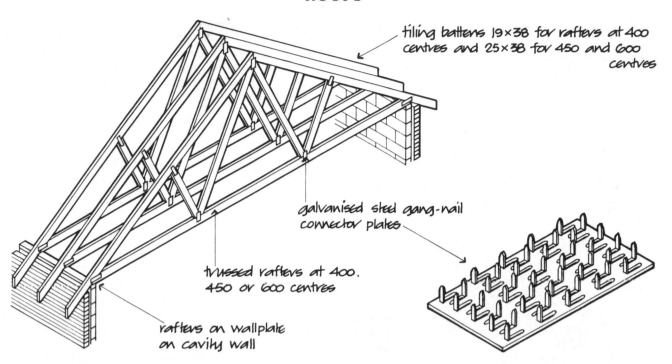

tiling battens 19×38 for rafters at 400 centres and 25×38 for 450 and 600 centres

galvanised steel gang-nail connector plates

trussed rafters at 400, 450 or 600 centres

rafters on wallplate on cavity wall

Trussed rafters for spans up to 12m and pitch from 15° to 40°

Fig. 169

The pitched roofs of terraced houses are commonly constructed with purlins the ends of which can be supported by walls dividing the houses. To prevent the spread of fire from one house to another, The Building Regulations require that the wall dividing houses, the party wall, be carried up to at least the level of the underside of the roof covering and purlins can be supported on brick or stone or concrete corbels built out from these walls. The construction is illustrated in Fig. 171.

Timber trusses: A strongly constructed purlin roof depends for support on loadbearing partitions conveniently placed and these partitions often restrict freedom in planning the rooms of the building. A method of constructing pitched roofs so as to avoid the use of struts to support purlins, and loadbearing partitions to support the struts, is to use timber trusses. The word truss means tied together and a timber roof truss is a triangular frame of light section timbers securely fixed together. The timber trusses span between external walls and are spaced about 1.8 apart and they serve to support purlins which in turn support the roof rafters. The most economical type of light section timber truss is that designed by the Timber Development Association. One of these trusses and the roof rafters is illustrated in Fig. 172. The size of timbers shown are for the span of roof illustrated, for larger spans slightly larger timber sizes are used. The timbers of the truss are bolted together and to make the connections rigid galvanised iron timber connectors are bolted between each two timbers at connections. The strength of the trusses derives mainly from the rigidity of the connections.

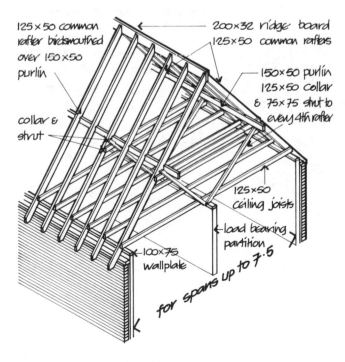

125×50 common rafter birdsmouthed over 150×50 purlin

collar & strut

200×32 ridge board
125×50 common rafters

150×50 purlin
125×50 collar & 75×75 strut to every 4th rafter

125×50 ceiling joists

load bearing partition

100×75 wallplate

for spans up to 7.5

Fig. 170

To reduce the quantity of timbers used the ceiling rafters are given support by means of hangers and binders. The hangers are nailed to the purlins and to these are nailed horizontal binders to which the ceiling joists are nailed or secured with metal plates.

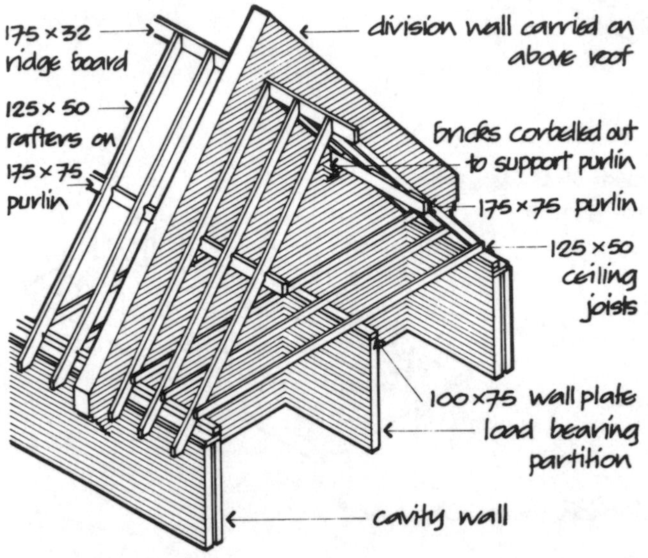

The timber connectors have opposed teeth as illustrated in Fig. 172. When the connector is firmly bolted between timbers it successfully prevents any scissor movement between them. The trusses bear on to timber wall plates bedded in mortar on the external walls and they support purlins which in turn support the rafters between the trusses.

Timber trusses have largely been superseded by trussed rafters for most domestic buildings.

Hips: The most economical way of constructing a pitched roof is to form it with two slopes with gable ends. But a simple gable end roof sometimes looks clumsy due to the great area of tile or slate covering and this can be avoided by forming hipped ends to the roof.

The hipped ends of roofs are pitched at the same slope as the main part of the roof and the rafters in the triangle of the hipped end are pitched up to a hip rafter. The hip rafters carry the ends of the cut rafters in the hipped end and those of the main roof slopes. The hip rafter is usually 38 thick and 200 to 250 deep. The cut 'jack rafters' are nailed each side of the hip rafter as shown in Fig. 173.

Because the hip rafter carries the ends of several jack rafters it tends to overturn the walls at the corner of the building where it bears on the wall plates and to resist this an angle tie should always be fixed across the angle of the roof as shown in Fig. 173.

175 × 32 ridge board

125 × 50 rafters on

175 × 75 purlin

division wall carried on above roof

binders corbelled out to support purlin

175 × 75 purlin

125 × 50 ceiling joists

100 × 75 wall plate

load bearing partition

cavity wall

Fig. 171

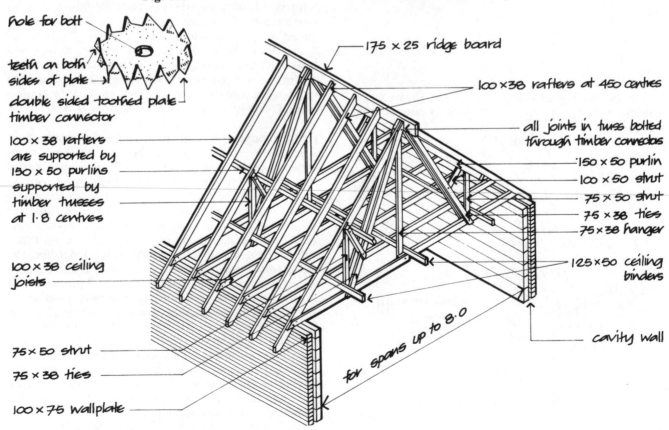

hole for bolt

teeth on both sides of plate

double sided toothed plate timber connector

100 × 38 rafters are supported by 150 × 50 purlins supported by timber trusses at 1·8 centres

100 × 38 ceiling joists

75 × 50 strut

75 × 38 ties

100 × 75 wallplate

175 × 25 ridge board

100 × 38 rafters at 450 centres

all joints in truss bolted through timber connectors

150 × 50 purlin

100 × 50 strut

75 × 50 strut

75 × 38 ties

75 × 38 hanger

125 × 50 ceiling binders

for spans up to 8·0

cavity wall

Fig. 172

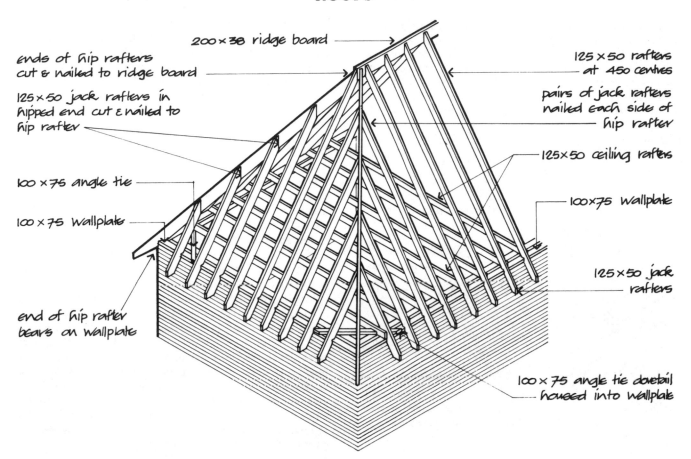

Fig. 173

The angle ties are usually 100×75 timber and are either firmly bolted to or dovetail housed into the top of the wall plates some 600 from the corner of the building. The dovetail housed joint is similar to that between a collar and rafters used in a collar roof.

Wind exclusion: One of the advantages of a pitched roof is that the triangular space inside the roof acts as an insulator against transference of heat. But if wind is able to blow through the tiles into the roof space it will prevent it from acting as an insulator. The cheapest method of keeping wind out is by covering the rafters with continuous layers of bitumen impregnated felt. Rolls of roofing felt, 813 wide, made from a mixture of animal and vegetable fibres impregnated with bitumen or tar are used. The rolls of felt are nailed across the roof rafters, under the battens, starting from the eaves and the felt is lapped 75 or 150 up to the roof so that if any water gets through the tiles it runs on to the felt and down the roof to the eaves.

The most effective way of keeping the space in a pitched roof dry and warm is to cover the roof rafters with softwood boarding. Boards 19 thick and between 150 and 225 wide are used and the boards are usually left rough from the saw. Plain edged boarding is generally used but the more expensive tongued and grooved boarding is used

where the roof space is used. The boarding is nailed to the rafters in the same way that floor boarding is nailed to joists. To prevent the possibility of any water which might get through the tiles causing the boarding to rot it is usual to lay roofing felt on top of it. If tiling battens were then fixed directly on to the felt and boards any water that got through the tiles would run down the felt and be trapped behind the battens and cause them to rot. To prevent this possibility counter battens are used. These are 38×19 or 50×25 sawn softwood and they are nailed to the boarding up the slope of the roof, the battens being fixed at about 450 to 600 centres and across them the tiling battens are nailed. The following view of part of a tiled roof will illustrate this construction (Fig. 174).

The use of roof boarding adds considerably to the cost of a tiled roof and is generally used only when the roof is to be used as a store or workroom.

Thermal insulation: The most economical and effective place to fix thermal insulation is at, over or under ceiling level of a pitched roof, where the area to be covered is less than that of the roof slope or slopes, and the roof space above acts as part of the total insulation.

Any one of the dry, rigid insulation boards may be fixed to the soffit of the ceiling, either as a ceiling finish or above a ceiling finish such as plasterboard, or mineral or glass fibre quilt may be draped over or between the ceiling joists above the ceiling or a dry fill spread on the ceiling joists as illustrated in Fig. 175. Some form of vapour barrier must be fixed, or be integral with the insulation on the warm side of the insulation to prevent moisture from warm air penetrating the insulating layer. Where a pitched roof covering, such as tile or slate, is laid over roof boarding or on sarking felt or paper the roof space acts as an insulator against transfer of heat.

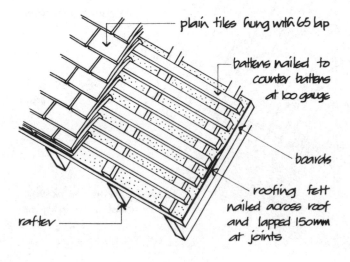

Fig. 174

PITCHED ROOF COVERINGS

The traditional covering for pitched roofs, plain clay tiles and natural slates, are much less used than they were because they are comparatively expensive and the majority of pitched roofs of new buildings are covered with single lap concrete tiles.

The small unit pitched roof coverings are single lap tiles, plain tiles and slates.

Tiles

Single lap tiles are so shaped that they overlap the edges of adjacent tiles in each course. This overlap prevents water entering the roof between adjacent tiles, and in consequence the tiles can be laid with a single end lap.

The advantage of single lap tiling is that its weight per unit of area of roof covered is up to 40% less than that of plain tiling of similar material and this provides for economy of roof structure.

Single lap tiles originated in the Mediterranian area as shaped clay tiles of half round section **Spanish tiles** overs and unders, Fig. 176, that were laid to side lap with a single lap down the slope as illustrated in Fig. 182, which were developed into the pantile, Fig. 176, which combined the channel and cover tile in one tile, and the **Italian tile**, Fig. 177, of a flat under and a half round section over, laid with a side lap and a single lap down the slope, as illustrated in Fig. 183, developed into the single Roman and double Roman tile, combining the under and over of the Italian tile in one tile, as illustrated in Fig. 177.

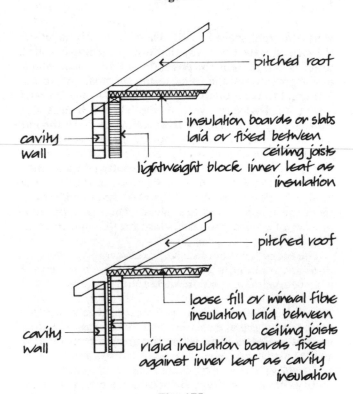

Fig. 175

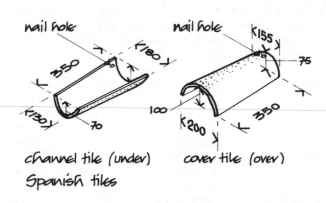

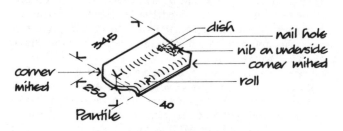

Fig. 176

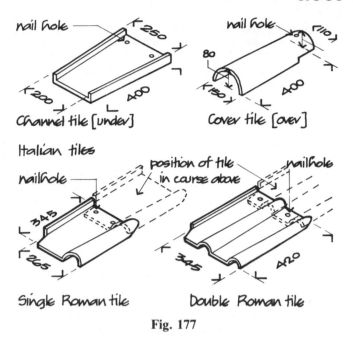

Italian tiles

Single Roman tile   Double Roman tile

Fig. 177

Concrete tiles are uniform in shape, texture and colour. The colours in which these tiles have so far been produced are very poor when compared with those of natural burned clay tiles. The colouring of these tiles is only in the top surface and in the course of time the colour tends to become washed out, leaving anaemic looking tiles. Concrete tiles are hard and dense and should be laid at slopes of from $17\frac{1}{2}°$ to $35°$ to the horizontal. A variety of shapes and sizes is manufactured as pantiles, flat interlocking and Roman tiles.

Clay roofing tiles: Clay can be excavated, moulded and burned without any expensive or elaborate machinery and for centuries clay roofing tiles have been used in this country.

In general two qualities of tile are manufactured (a) hand-made tiles, and (b) machine-pressed tiles.

Hand-made tiles are made from a sandy clay which is pressed into shape by hand pressure so that even if some form of screw press is used the clay is not very heavily compacted. During burning the tiles shrink and there are quite noticeable variations in shape and colour and it is these variations which give a tiled roof so attractive an appearance. The tiles vary in colour from light brick red to almost black and many of the more expensive tiles are sand faced to produce the rough texture which is popular.

Hand-made tiles fairly readily absorb water and should not be laid at a pitch of less than $45°$ to the horizontal. If laid at a less pitch these tiles may become saturated in winter and frost will then cause them to disintegrate. Machine-pressed tiles are made from selected pure clays which are thoroughly ground to a fine condition. The clay is mixed with very little water and is heavily machine-pressed into tiles. Because little water is used to make the clay sufficiently plastic for moulding the tiles do not shrink noticeably during burning and because the tiles are machine moulded they have smooth faces. These tiles are very hard and dense and do not absorb water readily and can be laid on a roof with a lower pitch than can the hand-made tiles. Machine-pressed tiles have successfully been laid at a pitch of as little as $30°$ to the horizontal but the minimum pitch for these tiles is generally accepted as being $35°$ to the horizontal. Because of their uniformity of shape, texture and colour, machine-pressed tiles do not make for so attractive a roof as the hand-made variety. Some machine-pressed tiles are faced with sand before being burned to give them a more attractive appearance. If clay roofing tiles have been made from clay which is free from lime and stones and the tiles have been hard burned and the tiles are laid at a suitable slope they will have a useful life of up to a hundred years or more. Good quality clay tiles weather well, which means they are resistant to damage by rain, frost, heat and all the dilute acids in industrial atmospheres.

Over the course of years the colour of clay tiles becomes somewhat darker and it is generally accepted that the appearance of a tile improves with age.

Plain tiles are flat, rectangular roofing units size 265 by 165 with holes for nailing and nibs for hanging to battens as illustrated in Fig. 178. These small tiles are laid double lap down the slope of the roof because water running between the open joints between adjacent tiles runs on to the back of a tile double lapped under the joint. A plain tile roof covering is generally heavier than a comparable single lap tile roof. Plain tiles are less used than they were.

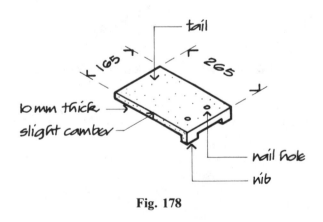

Fig. 178

Concrete roofing tiles are very extensively used today as a substitute for good quality clay tiles. The tiles are manufactured from a mixture of carefully graded sand, Portland cement and water which is compressed in a mould. A thin top dressing of sand, cement and colouring matter is then pressed into the top surface of the tile. The tiles are then left under cover for some days to allow them to harden.

Single lap tiling

The types of single lap tiling used in the United Kingdom are:

(a) Interlocking tiles.
(b) Pantiles in which the under and over of Spanish tiles is incorporated in one tile.
(c) Single and double Roman tiles in which the unders and overs of Italian tiles are incorporated in one tile.
(d) Spanish tiles consisting of pairs of rounded unders and overs.
(e) Italian tiles consisting of flat unders and rounded overs.

Single lap tiles with ordinary side lap are laid at a pitch of not less than 30° and concrete tiles with interlocking side lap at a patch of from 25° to 15°.

Interlocking single lap tiles: A range of interlocking concrete and clay single lap tiles is manufactured. The concrete tiles are made from the same materials and in a similar manner to concrete plain tiles. They differ from ordinary single lap tiles in that one or more grooves in the vertical edges of the tiles, Fig. 181, interlock when the tiles are laid. The advantage of this side lock is that it does more effectively exclude wind and rain than a simple overlap. Concrete interlocking side lap tiles are made in various colours such as red, green, yellow and grey.

Clay interlocking pantiles are made from selected pure clays which can be moulded and burned without any appreciable loss of shape. In consequence a sophisticated system of grooves at the sides and head of the tiles interlock with matching grooves on adjacent tiles, to provide a very efficient barrier to penetration of wind and rain. These tiles are made in a variety of colours such as green brown and red and also with various glazed colour finishes.

Pantiles: Concrete pantiles are used extensively in the United Kingdom. A typical concrete pantile is illustrated in Fig. 181. Clay pantiles are hung on and nailed to softwood battens as illustrated in Fig. 179. The purpose of the mitred corners of these tiles is to facilitate fixing. But for the mitred corners there would be four thicknesses of tile at the junction of horizontal and vertical joints which would make it impossible to bed the tiles properly.

Single and double Roman tiles: Clay Roman tiles are less used than they were. The tiles are hung on and nailed to softwood battens as illustrated in Fig. 180.

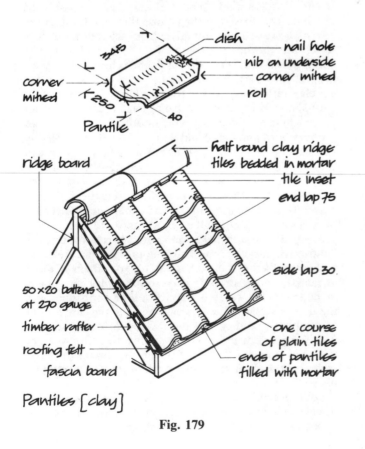

Pantiles [clay]

Fig. 179

Single Roman tile

Double Roman tile

Roman tiles [clay]

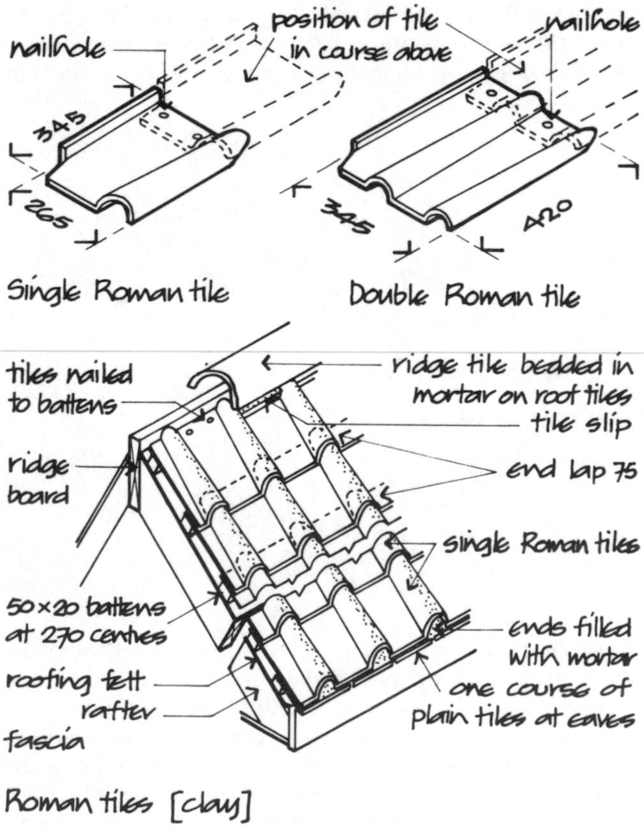

Fig. 180

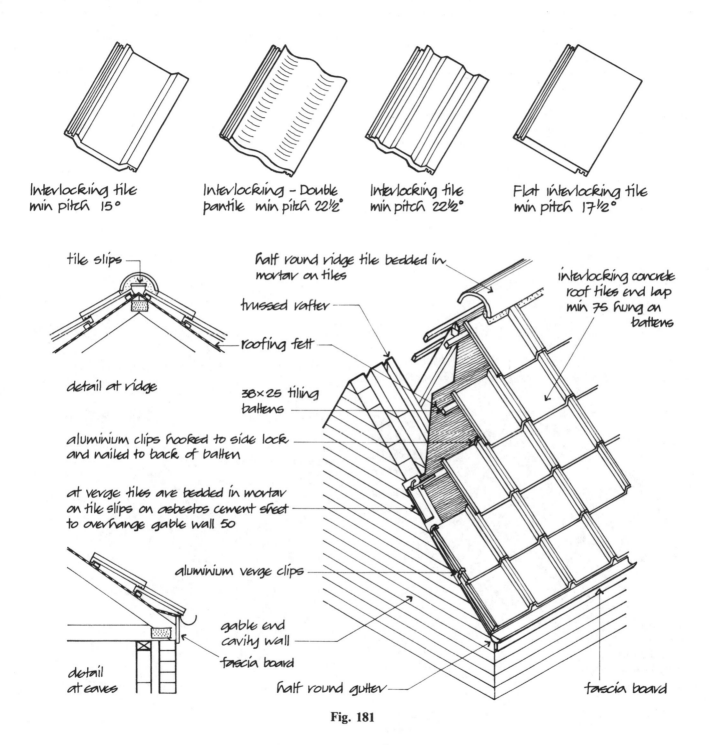

Interlocking tile
min pitch 15°

Interlocking – Double
pantile min pitch 22½°

Interlocking tile
min pitch 22½°

Flat interlocking tile
min pitch 17½°

tile slips

detail at ridge

aluminium clips hooked to side lock
and nailed to back of batten

at verge tiles are bedded in mortar
on tile slips on asbestos cement sheet
to overhange gable wall 50

detail
at eaves

half round ridge tile bedded in
mortar on tiles

trussed rafter

roofing felt

38×25 tiling
battens

aluminium verge clips

gable end
cavity wall

fascia board

half round gutter

interlocking concrete
roof tiles end lap
min 75 hung on
battens

fascia board

Fig. 181

103

Spanish tiles: These are made from natural clays. Few of these tiles are used in this country because they are laborious to fix and make a comparatively heavy roof covering. These tiles are made as pairs of rounded tapering unders and overs as shown in Fig. 182. They are fixed to softwood battens which are nailed to boarding up the slope of the roof. The unders are nailed to the sides of battens and overs to top of battens, as shown in Fig. 182.

Italian tiles: These clay tiles are little used in this country. The flat unders are nailed to roof boarding and the rounded overs to vertical softwood battens as illustrated in Fig. 183.

Ridges: At the ridge the space between the edge of the ridge tiles and the back of single lap tiles is filled with mortar in which slips of tile are bedded. These tile slips are cut from plain tiles and serve to minimise cracking of the comparatively thick mortar filling.

Eaves: To provide a level bed on which mortar can be spread and onto which the single lap tiles can be bedded one course of plain tiles is fixed at eaves. The four types of clay single lap tiles are made in various colours such as red, brown, purple and grey and also with glazed finishes in certain colours.

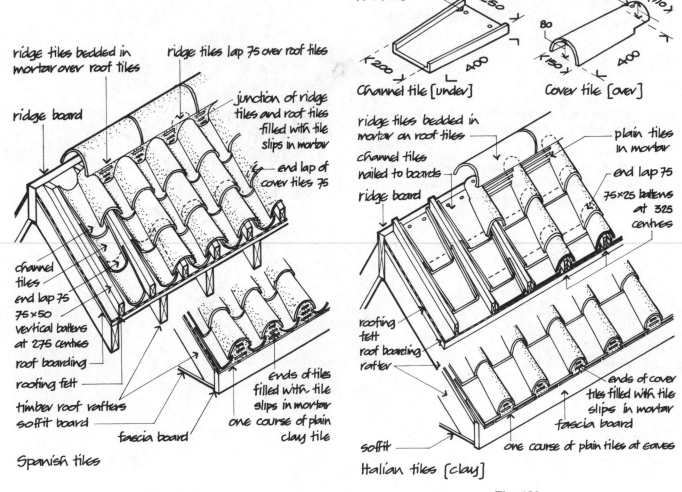

Fig. 182

Fig. 183

Plain tiles

Size of plain tiles: The standard size of these tiles is 265 long by 165 wide and not less than 10 thick. These rather peculiar sizes derive, it seems, from 'An Act for the making of Tile' passed in 1477, in the reign of Edward IV. The Act required, among other things, that the tile be $10\frac{1}{2}$ in long, $6\frac{1}{4}$ in wide and between $\frac{1}{2}$ in and $\frac{1}{8}$ in thick. The Act was passed because tile makers were producing tiles of various sizes and this led to difficulties when roofs were being repaired.

Nibs: Standard plain clay tiles today have projecting nibs at one end of the tile or one continuous nib. The tiles are secured to the sloping surface of the roof by hanging them by these nibs to horizontally fixed timber battens. A view of a plain tile is shown in Fig. 184.

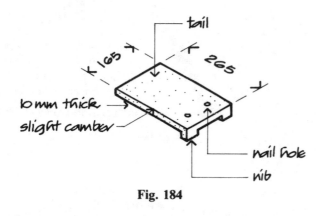

Fig. 184

Camber: The tiles are not perfectly flat but have a slight rise or camber in the back of them. The purpose of this camber is to prevent water being drawn up between the tiles by capillary action, as it would be if the tiles were absolutely flat.

Gauge and lap: Plain tiles are hung on 38×19 or 50×25 sawn softwood battens which are nailed across the rafters of the roof. The tiles are hung so that at every point on the roof there are at least two thicknesses of tile. This is illustrated in the view of part of a tiled roof shown in Fig. 185.

It will be seen that the tiles are hung so that their sides butt together and these joints are bonded up the slope of the roof. The tiles in every fourth course are nailed to the battens. This is a precaution to ensure that in high wind the tiles are not lifted off the roof. In very exposed positions every tile should be nailed to the battens. Each tile lies over the tile below it and also some 65 over the head of the tile below that. It is obvious that tiles must at least lie over half the length of the tile below to prevent water running between the butt side joints into the roof below. Plain tiles are laid double lap to prevent rain running off the back of one tile, in the joint between the two tiles below and then spreading out between tiles so that it runs into the roof. Figure 186 shows a few tiles

laid without double lap. It will be seen that water creeps between tiles B. and D., and C. and D. and runs in over the head of tiles E. and F. The lap has to be made sufficient to prevent this.

The angle at which water spreads out between the tiles depends mainly on the slope of the tiles. The steeper the slope the less water will spread out. The usual lap for plain tiles is 65. For this lap tiles 265 long have to be hung at 100 intervals up the slope of the roof. The battens must therefore be fixed at intervals of 100. The distance between the centres of the battens is described as the gauge.

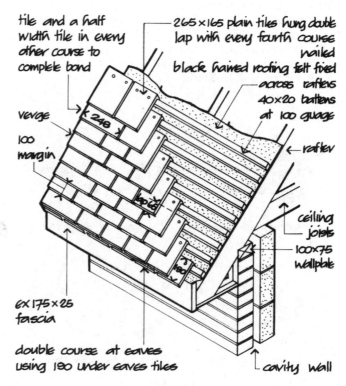

Fig. 185

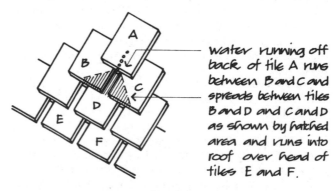

Fig. 186

Eaves: So that there are two thicknesses of tile at the eaves a course of eaves tile is used. These tiles are 190 long and 165 wide and are the first course of tiles to be hung as illustrated in Fig. 185. The tails of the eaves tiles and the tile course above overhang the fascia board some 40 to shed water into the eaves gutter.

Ridge: Any one of four standard sections of clay ridge tile may be used to cover the ridge. The four standard sections of clay ridge tile are illustrated in Fig. 187. Tile courses are hung up to the ridge board and a special top course of tiles 190 long is used. The ridge tiles, whichever of the four sections is used, have their edges bedded in fillets of cement mortar spread on the back of the top course tiles. The ridge tiles butt together and so that the joint can be satisfactorily filled with mortar the ends of all ridge tiles are solidly filled with mortar. This prevents the mortar in the joints from falling in. A section through a tiled ridge is illustrated in Fig. 188.

illustrated in Fig. 189. Each tile is nailed to the hip rafter and the open ends of the tiles are filled with cement mortar. Of the two sections the bonnet hip gives the most pleasing finish to a roof as the curve of its tail carries the line of the tiles smoothly over the hip as illustrated in Fig. 190.

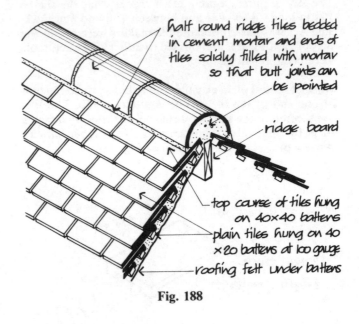

half round ridge tiles bedded in cement mortar and ends of tiles solidly filled with mortar so that butt joints can be pointed

ridge board

top course of tiles hung on 40×40 battens

plain tiles hung on 40 × 20 battens at 100 gauge

roofing felt under battens

Fig. 188

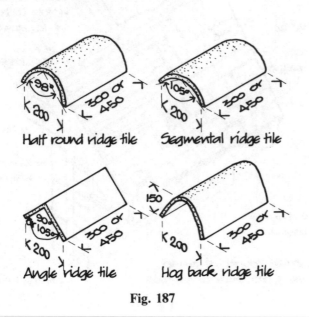

Half round ridge tile   Segmental ridge tile

Angle ridge tile   Hog back ridge tile

Fig. 187

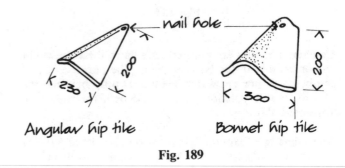

nail hole

Angular hip tile   Bonnet hip tile

Fig. 189

Hips: The hips can be covered with ridge tiles bedded in exactly the same way that they are on ridges. To prevent the tiles slipping down the hip a galvanised iron or wrought-iron hip iron is fixed to the hip or fascia. The plain tiles next to the hip have to be cut to fit against the side of the hip rafter so that they lie under the hip tiles.

The tiles which are cut to the side of the hip are usually cut from special tile-and-a-half tiles which are 248 wide by 265 long. These tile-and-a-half width tiles have three nibs so that after being cut there is a nib to hang them on. A hip covered with ridge tiles has a poor appearance.

Hip tiles are manufactured which can be nailed to the hip rafter so that they lap one over the other and the tail of these tiles lines up with the courses of plain tiles on the roof. The two standard sections of hip tiles are

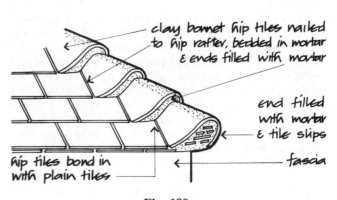

clay bonnet hip tiles nailed to hip rafter, bedded in mortar & ends filled with mortar

end filled with mortar & tile slips

fascia

hip tiles bond in with plain tiles

Fig. 190

Verge: The verge of plain tiling at a gable end of a roof is usually bedded on the gable end wall and tilted up slightly to prevent water running off the tiles down the gable end wall. Tile-and-a-half width tiles are used in every other course to complete the bond. The construction of a tiled verge is illustrated in Fig. 191.

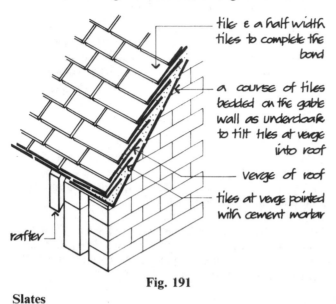

tile ε a half width tiles to complete the bond

a course of tiles bedded on the gable wall as undercloak to tilt tiles at verge into roof

verge of roof

tiles at verge pointed with cement mortar

rafter

Fig. 191

Slates

Roofing slates There are three sorts of roofing slate in common use (a) Welsh slates; (b) Westmorland slates; (c) asbestos cement slates.

Welsh slates are extensively quarried in the mountains of Wales. The stone from which they are split is hard and dense and varies in colour from light grey to purple. In the quarry the stone consists of thin layers of laminae of hard slate with a very thin somewhat softer layer of slate between the layers. By driving a wedge of steel into the stone between the layers it can be quickly split into fairly large quite thin slates of thicknesses varying from 4 to 10. The splitting results in slates of varying thickness and the thicker slates are classified as best, strong best, and medium, and the thinner slates as seconds and thirds. There is no agreed minimum thickness for the above classification which therefore seems somewhat pointless. The slates are cut to a variety of sizes varying from 610 long by 355 wide to 255 × 150. The most commonly used sizes are 610 × 355, 510 × 255, 460 × 230 and 405 × 205. For many years each size of slate was given a particular name, such as Countess for the 510 × 255 slates. No useful purpose is served in giving a name to each specific size of slate and it is hoped that before long naming of slate sizes will be discontinued.

Good quality Welsh slates are hard and dense and do not readily absorb water. They are not affected by frost or the dilute acids in industrial atmospheres and will have a useful life as a roof covering of very many years. The durability of a slate depends upon its density and the most reliable guide to this is the amount of water it will absorb if immersed in water for a set time. Slates which absorb the least water will have a useful life as a roof covering of a hundred years or more, and can be laid at a slope of as little as 25° to the horizontal.

Westmorland slates are quarried from stone in the mountain region of the Lake District. The stone varies in colour from blue to green with flecks and streaks of browns and greys. The stone is very hard and dense, and consists of irregular layers or laminae of hard stone, separated by very slightly softer stone. The laminae do not run in regular flat planes as in Welsh slate and the stone is more difficult to split than the Welsh. As a consequence it is not so economic to split slates and cut them to uniform size and Westmorland slates are commonly used in random sizes. These slates are split to thicknesses of from 7 to 19 and the slates have rough surfaces and sharp irregular edges.

The best quality Westmorland slates are very hard and so dense that they absorb practically no water no matter how long they are immersed in water. These slates are practically indestructible. Because of the considerable labour required to cut the stone Westmorland slates are expensive and generally only used for more expensive building works.

Asbestos cement slates are manufactured in sizes similar to the size of Welsh slates and are used in the same way. These slates are cheaper than the natural material.

Fixing slates: Slates are fixed to 50 × 25 sawn softwood battens by means of copper composition nails driven through holes which are punched in the head of each slate. Galvanised iron or iron nails should not be used as they will in time rust and allow the slates to slip out of position. Two holes are punched in each slate some 25 from the head of the slate and about 40 in from the side of the slate as illustrated in Fig. 192. The battens are nailed across the roof rafters and the slates nailed to them so that at every point on the roof there are at least two thicknesses of slate and so that the tail of each slate laps 75 over the head of the slate two courses below. This is similar to the double lap arrangement of plain tiles and is done for the same reason so that slates are double lapped. Because the length of slates vary and the lap is usually constant it is necessary to calculate the spacing or gauge of the battens. The formula for this calculation is:

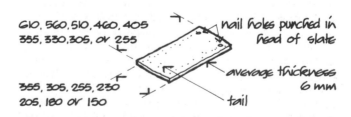

610, 560, 510, 460, 405
355, 330, 305, or 255

355, 305, 255, 230
205, 180 or 150

nail holes punched in head of slate

average thickness 6 mm

tail

Fig. 192

$$gauge = \frac{length\ of\ slate - (lap + 25)}{2}.$$

For example the gauge of the spacing of the battens for 510 × 255 slates is:

$$\frac{510 - (75 + 25)}{2} = 205.$$

The following drawing illustrates the fixing of slates to a pitched roof (Fig. 193).

Roofing felt should be nailed across the rafters under the battens to keep wind out of the roof.

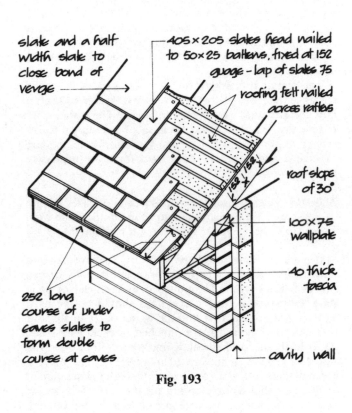

Fig. 193

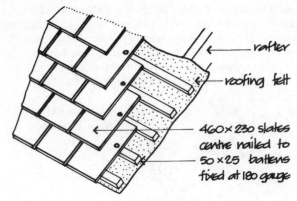

Fig. 194

When roof boarding is used to keep the roof space wind tight the slates, whether head or centre nailed, are usually nailed directly to the boarding through the roofing felt as illustrated in Fig. 195.

Eaves: So that there shall be two thicknesses of slates at the eaves a course of undereaves slate is used. These slates are cut to a length equal to the gauge + lap + 25 of the slating as illustrated in Fig. 193.

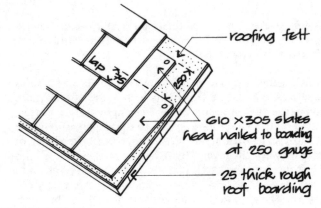

Fig. 195

Head nailed and centre nailed slates: Slates are usually fixed by means of nails driven through holes in the head of slates. This is the best method of fixing slates as the nail holes are covered with two thicknesses of slate so that even if one slate cracks water will not get in. But if long slates such as 610 × 305 are head nailed on a shallow slope of say 30° or less it is possible that in high wind the slates may be lifted so much that they snap off at the nail holes. In exposed positions on low pitch roofs it is common to fix the slates by centre nailing them to battens. The nails are not driven through holes exactly in the centre of the length of the slate but at a distance equal to the gauge down from head of slate, so that the slate can double lap at tails as illustrated in Fig. 194. It will be seen that with this method of fixing there is only one thickness of slate over each nail hole so that if that slate cracks water can get into the roof.

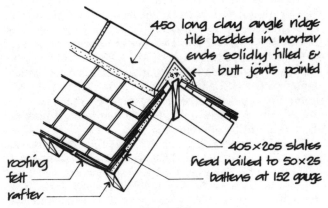

Fig. 196

108

Ridge: The cheapest way of covering the ridge of slated roofs is to use one of the clay ridge tiles which are bedded and pointed as they are on the ridge of a tiled roof. The top course of slates is usually shorter than the ordinary slates, being gauge + lap + 50 or 75 in length, as illustrated in Fig. 196. Another method of covering a slate ridge is to finish it with strips of lead sheet dressed over a wood roll and secured with lead clips as shown in Fig. 197.

Hips: These are covered with either ridge tiles or lead sheet in the same way that the ridge is covered.

Verge: At the verge of a slate slope, slate-and-a-half width slates are used to complete the bond and the slates are tilted up slightly as are tiles at the verge of a tiled roof.

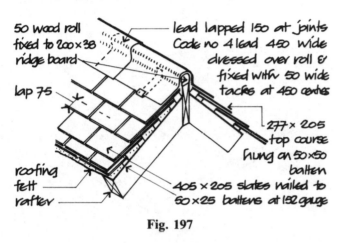

Fig. 197

Sheet metal coverings to pitched roofs

Of recent years it has been common practice to construct low pitched roofs for houses, schools and other buildings. A pitched roof is generally defined as one with slopes of 10° or more to the horizontal and a low pitched roof has slopes of from 10° to 30° to the horizontal. The disadvantages of a flat roof have already been mentioned and a steeply pitched roof is not always an attractive feature of small buildings. For example a small bungalow with a pitched roof covered with tiles does not usually look attractive as the great area of tiles dominates the lesser area of wall below. A low pitched roof is a happy compromise between flat and steeply pitched roofs. It at once looks attractive, gives reasonable insulation against loss of heat and provides roof space in which water storage tanks can be housed.

The principal coverings for low pitched roofs are copper and aluminium strips, both of which are comparatively light in weight and therefore do not require heavy timbers to support them and both have a useful life as a roof covering of many years. The roofs are constructed as single slope roofs or as low pitched roofs with timber rafters pitched to a central ridge board with or without hipped ends. The construction of the rafters and their support with purlins and struts, or purlins and light

timber trusses is similar to that for other pitched roofs as previously explained.

Copper or aluminium strips of 450 or 600 width and up to 8.0 long are used to cover these low pitched roofs. No drips or double lock cross welts or other joints transverse to the fall are used with strips up to 8.0 long and because of this the labour in jointing the sheets is less than that required with batten or conical roll systems of covering and because of this copper or aluminium strip coverings are comparatively cheap. Because of the great length of each strip the fixing cleats used to hold the metal strips in position have to be designed to allow the metal to contract and expand freely.

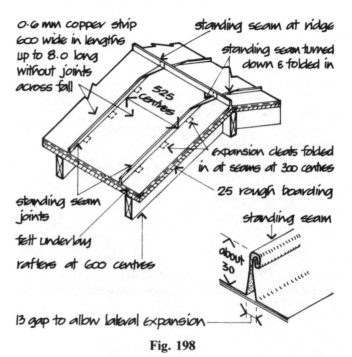

Fig. 198

Standing seams: The strips of metal are jointed down the slope of the roof by means of a standing seam joint which is a form of double welt and is left standing up from the roof as shown in Fig. 198, which is a view of part of a low pitched roof. The completed standing seam is constructed so that there is a gap of some 13 at its base which allows the metal to expand without restraint and this is illustrated in Fig. 198. The lightweight metal strips have to be secured to the roof surface at intervals of 300 along the length of the standing seams. This close spacing of the fixing cleats is necessary to prevent the metal drumming in windy weather.

Two types of cleats are used, fixed cleats and expansion cleats. Five fixed cleats are fixed in the centre of the length of each strip and the rest of the cleats are expansion cleats. Figure 199 illustrates the arrangement of these cleats. The fixed cleats are nailed to the roof boarding through the felt underlay and Fig. 199 illustrates the formation of a standing seam and shows how the fixed cleat is folded in.

The expansion cleats are made of two pieces of copper strip folded together so that one part can be nailed to the roof and the second piece, which is folded in at the standing seam, can move inside the fixed piece. Figure 199 illustrates one type of expansion cleat used.

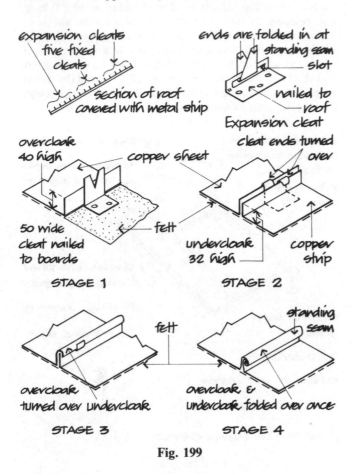

Fig. 199

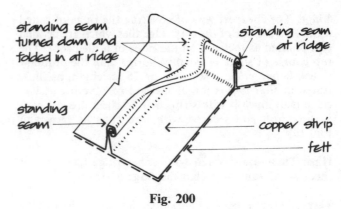

Fig. 200

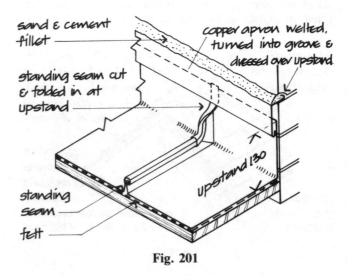

Fig. 201

Ridge: The ridge is usually finished with a standing seam joint as illustrated in Fig. 198, but as an alternative a batten roll or conical roll may be used. Whichever joint is used at the ridge the standing seams on the slopes of the roof have to be turned down so that they can be folded in at the ridge. This is illustrated in Fig. 200.

Where the slope of the roof finishes at the parapet or wall the strips of metal are turned up as an upstand and finished with an apron flashing. This is illustrated in Fig. 201 which also illustrates the cutting and turning down of the standing seam.

Eaves: Because copper or aluminium are generally considered to be attractive coverings to roofs, the roof is not hidden behind a parapet wall, and the roof slopes discharge to an eaves gutter as illustrated in Fig. 202.

Verge: The verge of low pitched roofs can be finished with batten roll or conical roll as previously illustrated for flat roof coverings.

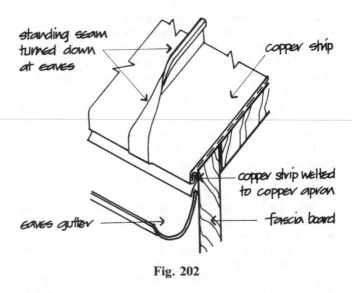

Fig. 202

Felt underlay: It is vital that strip metal coverings be laid on an underlay of bitumen-impregnated roofing felt laid across the roof boards and nailed to the boards with butt side joints. The felt allows the metal strips to expand and contract without restraint.

INDEX

INDEX

INDEX

INDEX